THE HUMAN SPECIES

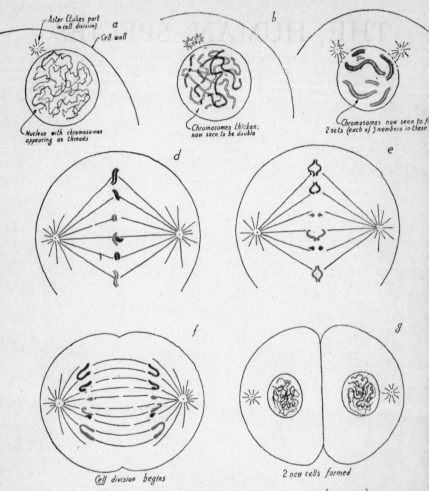

a — Aster (takes part in cell division) — Cell wall — Nucleus with chromosomes appearing as threads

b — Chromosomes thicken; now seen to be double

c — Chromosomes now seen to f 2 sets (each of 3 members in these

d

e

f — Cell division begins

g — 2 new cells formed

DIVISION OF THE NUCLEUS OF AN EGG-CELL (MITOSIS)

The nucleus when not dividing appears as a structureless, roughly spherical object ; when division begins the chromosomes become visible as double threads ; the members of each pair separate, and two daughter-nuclei are formed, each with the same number of chromosomes as the parent nucleus. The whole cell then divides, and each daughter-cell gets one nucleus. This happens throughout the body in the cells of growing tissues. The number of chromosomes is here shown as only three pairs, for simplicity ; man has 24 pairs. (See p. 9, and Plate I opposite p. 16)

THE
Human
Species

A Biology of Man

by

ANTHONY BARNETT

W. W. NORTON & COMPANY INC. *New York*

First Published, April 1950

Copyright 1950
W. W. Norton & Company Inc.   *New York*
Manufactured in England
Set in 11/12 Baskerville and
Printed at Pettys Press by
C. Nicholls & Company, Ltd.
Reading, London and Manchester
and Bound by
G. & J. Kitcat Ltd., London

ACKNOWLEDGMENTS

I owe a special debt to Dr. M. L. Johnson and Michael Abercrombie, for reading and criticising the manuscript and for many stimulating discussions.

I am also very grateful to Professor W. E. Le Gros Clark for finding time to discuss problems that arose in the writing of the book, and for providing up-to-date information and material.

Richard Palmer read the whole book in draft, Dr. John Humphrey the chapter on disease, and Dr. J. S. Weiner the chapters on human evolution and on race. I am very grateful to all of these for their expert advice.

I wish also to thank A. G. Jenson, F.R.I.B.A., and Edward Walton, who drew the diagrams, for their skill and patience.

S. A. B.

Acknowledgment is due also to the following authors and publishers for permission to reproduce illustrations either in the original or a modified form :

Frontispiece and p. 10 : after *Genetics, Medicine and Man*, by H. J. Muller and others (Oxford U.P. ; Cornell U.P.) ; p. 15 : *Genetics in Relation to Agriculture*, by E. B. Babcock and R. E. Clausen (McGraw Hill) ; pp. 31 & 33 : after *Heredity and Politics*, by J. B. S. Haldane (Allen & Unwin) ; pp. 36 & 37 : after *Human Genetics*, by R. R. Gates (Constable, London ; Macmillan, N.Y.) ; pp. 42, 43, 47, 51, 53 & 59 : after *The Hormones in Human Reproduction*, by G. W. Corner (Oxford U.P., Princeton U.P.) ; pp. 55 & 62 : after *From Head to Foot*, by A. Novikoff (Lawrence & Wishart, London ; International Publishers, N.Y.) ; pp. 74, 75, 78, 80, 81, 82 & 83 : *Mankind so Far*, by W. Howells (Sigma, London ; Doubleday, N.Y.) ; pp. 88 & 91 : after the same ; p. 124 : *Introduction to Medical Genetics*, by J. A. F. Roberts (Oxford U.P.) ; p. 127 : *Introduction to Modern Genetics*, by C. H. Waddington (Allen & Unwin) ; p. 129 : *The Nation's Intelligence*, by J. L. Gray (Watts) ; pp. 166, 177 & 188 : after *World Food Survey 1946* (F.A.O.) ; p. 193 : *Food, Health and Income*, by J. B. Orr (Macmillan) ; p. 214 : *Medicine and Mankind*, by A. Sorsby (Faber) ; pp. 215, 218, 219 & 230 : after *A*

v

Acknowledgments *continued*

Charter for Health (B.M.A.) ; pp. 226 & 227 : J. Hyg. Camb. (1945), B. Woolf & M. Waterhouse (Cambridge U.P.) ; pp. 234 & 238 : after *Handbook of Sociology*, by W. F. Ogburn & M. F. Nimkoff (Routledge & Kegan Paul) ; p. 241 : *Plenty of People*, by W. S. Thompson (Jacques Cattell Press) ; p. 244 : *The Future Population of Europe*, by F. W. Notestein (League of Nations) ; p. 246 : *Statistical Year Book 1945* (League of Nations) ; p. 250 : *A Future for Preventive Medicine*, by E. J. Steiglitz (Oxford U.P. ; Commonwealth Fund, N.Y.) ; p. 253 : after *Parents Revolt*, by R. M. & K. Titmuss (Secker & Warburg).

PLATES : 1. Dr. P. C. Koller ; 3. *Albinism in Man*, by K. Pearson, E. Nettleship & C. H. Usher (Cambridge U.P.) : 4. *The Tissues of the Body*, by W. E. Le Gros Clark (Clarendon) ; 5. *Race, Reason and Rubbish*, by G. Dahlberg (Allen & Unwin) ; 2 & 6. Genetica (1928), J. P. Lotsy & W. A. Goddijn (Martinus Nijhoff) ; 7, 8, 10, 11 & 12. Pitt Rivers Museum, Oxford ; 9. Alexander Lipschutz ; 13 & 14a. U.S. Information Service, London ; 14b & 15. U.S. Soil Conservation Service and *The Rape of the Earth*, by G. V. Jacks & R. O. Whyte (Faber) ; 16. K.P.M. Line, Amsterdam.

CONTENTS

ILLUSTRATIONS

PLATES

DRAWINGS & DIAGRAMS

Illustrations *continued*

WHAT IS BIOLOGY?

WHAT IS BIOLOGY?

Amoeba has her picture in the book,
Proud protozoon !—Yet beware of pride.
All she can do is fatten and divide ;
She cannot even read or sew or cook . . .

JULIAN HUXLEY

THIS book describes some of the contributions that biological knowledge can make to contemporary problems. It has been written, and will be read, at a time of social upheaval, and it has not been designed as a detached, disinterested account of man, such as a biologist might give of a dung beetle or an earthworm.

Biology began when men first distinguished between useful and dangerous plants and animals. Every branch of scientific knowledge has an origin in man's attempts to satisfy his material needs ; biology, the science of living things, is most closely linked to the production of food and the prevention of disease.

Accurate biological knowledge is thus very much older than civilisation, but the systematic and deliberate study of plants and animals is a recent affair. Apart from rather isolated individuals, such as Aristotle in classical times, or Albertus Magnus in the middle ages, the first biologists appeared about three centuries ago, in western Europe. Interest in the variety of living things had been greatly stimulated by new discoveries abroad. New types of timber, new fur-bearing animals, new fruits and foods of all kinds made an interest in at least one aspect of biology profitable. To ensure the full benefit from these discoveries an agreed classification and system of names for all known living things were needed. As a result, in the eighteenth century, many biologists turned their attention to the classification and naming of plants and animals.

The foremost of these was Linnaeus. Our present system of giving each species two Latin names is largely due to him. Thus while a common British bird may be called a lapwing, a peewit or a plover in English alone, and other names in other languages, in scientific works in all languages it is called *Vannellus vannellus*. Similarly, there are two common species of flowering plant called "cuckoo-flower"; one of them is also called "lady's smock", but it has only one Latin name : *Cardamine pratensis*.

Among the new things found in different lands were unfamiliar types of men. Linnaeus nevertheless recognised that all human beings belong to one species, and named the species *Homo sapiens*—thinking man. This is the species with which this book is concerned. But although man will here be studied from the point of view of a biologist, this does not imply that human needs and desires will be ignored. Human biology is a branch of knowledge that can be of practical value to every human being. Health and disease, food, the sizes and quality of human populations, the diversity of human types and their abilities, are all topics on which knowledge is not only desirable, but, for a twentieth-century adult, necessary.

This treatment of biology, centred on man and based on the usefulness of biological knowledge, is the opposite of the conventional one. Even the relatively few who have studied biology at school will find most of the facts in this book unfamiliar. In the schools we may learn in detail about a sea-weed called *Fucus*, which is not even edible, let alone important ; but often little is heard of man's biggest industry, agriculture, on which we depend for food. In the animal kingdom we may begin with the study of an obscure microscopic organism called *Amoeba*, but perhaps learn nothing of the related malarial parasite, although malaria is probably the worst of all the infectious diseases. The earthworm is studied in detail, but the important part it plays in making soil fertile may go unmentioned. Among insects attention is usually concentrated on the cockroach, which happens to be a minor pest though this fact is often not to be found in the textbooks ; the many serious insect pests are ignored. When we come to the group to which man belongs, the vertebrates, the chosen example is commonly the frog, a vertebrate of many highly unusual characteristics, and of negligible economic importance.

Some teachers are trying to change all this, and not all biology courses ignore the practical significance of the subject ;

2

but many must leave the impression that biology is largely an academic study, of interest only to those concerned with knowledge for its own sake.

In this book the attempt is made to relate the main facts of human biology to the problems facing us in the middle of the twentieth century. The second chapter, on nature and nurture (or heredity and environment) deals with a topic which underlies much of the rest of the book. It is sometimes asserted that human nature cannot change : what this statement could mean, and whether it is true, is part of the subject matter of the chapter. The third deals in more detail with some aspects of human genetics. These two are the most difficult chapters. They are followed by one which completes the story of human reproduction and development.

After them there are five chapters on the evolution of man, and the differences between groups of men (or races) and between individual men and women today. Most people know that men are descended from ape-like ancestors, but few know what the evidence for this statement is, or how the process has taken place. Everyone knows that man exists in many shapes and colours ; that some men are stupid, others intelligent ; some criminal, others virtuous. These facts raise a number of urgent social problems, to some of which biological knowledge can suggest a solution. Finally, there is a series of chapters on various aspects of human populations. Like other animals man must, in order to survive, overcome the dangers of starvation and infection ; at the same time he must be fertile. Four chapters therefore deal with food, disease and the growth and decline of human populations.

This scheme may be criticised on the grounds that it omits an account of those human characteristics which distinguish man most clearly and sharply from other animals : the point might be expressed by saying that human *behaviour* is ignored ; or some might say that human *psychology* is left out, or that no account is taken of the human *mind*. This aspect of man is here dealt with only cursorily, not because little importance is attached to it, but because it is so important that it needs another book of similar size even for a summary account. Language alone requires far lengthier treatment than could be given here. On the other hand, no apology is offered for the objective treatment of human problems. A doctor taking the pulse-rate of a patient is making an objective measurement in the same way as an engineer observing the revolutions of an engine, and nobody criticises him for doing so. Human beings are very much more complex than any machine, but that need not deter us from being matter-of-fact about ourselves.

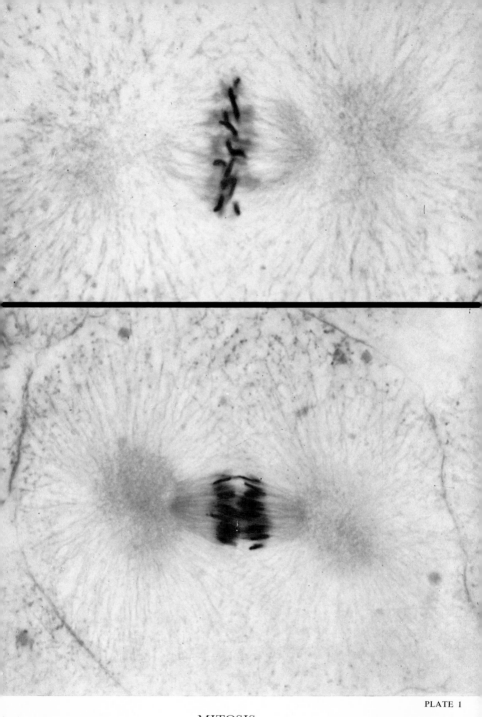

PLATE 1

MITOSIS

Photomicrographs of the division of the nucleus in the cell of a fish. *Above,* the nucleus has condensed into its constituent chromosomes ; *below,* the two groups of daughter chromosomes are separating, to form two new nuclei. Compare frontispiece

PLATE 2

NEGRO-WHITE CROSSING

The family of a Scottish-Griqua woman who married a white man :
her sons show various combinations of characters (described on
page 27)

PLATE 3

ALBINO CHILDREN

Albinos have no skin or hair pigment ; the condition is due to a recessive gene, like red hair, but it differs from red hair in being disadvantageous, since there is excessive sensitivity to light

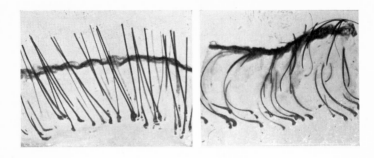

HAIR TYPES

Photomicrographs of human scalp showing mode of growth of hair :
left, in a Chinese, with straight hair of the Mongoloid type ; *right,* in
a Bushman, with coiled hair of negroid type

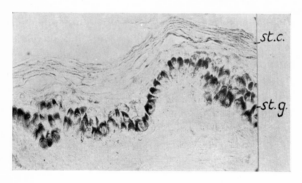

PLATE 4

NEGRO SKIN

Photomicrograph through a thin slice or section : the dead,
cornified surface layer (st. c.) overlies a layer of living cells containing black pigment (st. g.). Variation in the amount of this pigment
causes the variation in human "colour"

Part One

HEREDITY AND REPRODUCTION

THE differences between individual human beings depend partly on what we inherit from our parents, partly on differences of environment : heredity and environment interact in complex ways to produce the end-product of the adult individual. Neither heredity nor environment has a greater influence, but when we come to practical action we can influence environment, for instance nutrition or working conditions, while for man heredity has generally to be accepted.

The great variety of inherited differences is maintained by the mixing of the inherited factors, or genes, in sexual reproduction. The genes are transmitted from parent to offspring in microscopic structures, the chromosomes, which are present in the sperm and egg and also in every cell of the adult body. The regular behaviour of the chromosomes determines laws of heredity which apply to man and throughout the animal and plant kingdoms.

Sexual reproduction entails a complex development from a minute fertilised egg. In man the first forty weeks of life are spent as a parasite within the mother, and the physiological processes which take place in mother and child are now coming to be understood, with results of great importance to the individual and society.

CHAPTER 2

NATURE AND NURTURE

A devil, a born devil, upon whose nature
Nurture will never stick.
WILLIAM SHAKESPEARE :
(Prospero on Caliban)

IT is sometimes said by Europeans that all Chinese look alike. Doubtless few take this statement seriously ; certainly, it is very far from the truth. In every human group individuals differ from each other both physically and mentally. There are two sources of this variation : in the first place individuals differ in the factors handed on from their parents, the *inherited* factors as they may be called ; second, the influences that act on the individual from outside, and make up his *environment*, are highly variable. The study of these effects, that is, of heredity and variation, is called *genetics*. Human genetics is the subject of this and the next chapter.

If a child has insufficient iodine in his food he fails to grow normally and becomes a dwarf, of the type known as a cretin. This used to happen a good deal in Switzerland, and it is an example of environment influencing growth ; a simple alteration in the environment, the addition of iodine to table salt, prevented the effect. But similar dwarfs occasionally appear in communities in which there is no lack of iodine, and no alteration in the amount of iodine in the food, or in any other environmental agency, affects their occurrence. In this case the condition is said to be due to heredity. These two examples show that stature can be affected by both environment and heredity.

HEREDITY (OR "NATURE")

The word heredity is used here in a slightly unfamiliar way. If a tall father has a tall son, it is sometimes said that the son inherits his tallness from his father. We shall see later what really does happen. But the case of the dwarfism due to heredity is different, since the parents of the dwarf are them-

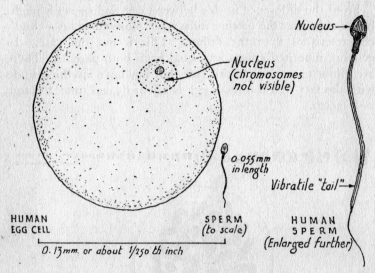

EGG AND SPERM

Human egg-cell, with sperm-cell drawn to scale, and larger drawing of a sperm-cell

selves normal : there is no question of the dwarfism being inherited from one of the parents in the usual sense. This sort of thing is quite familiar from our experience of normal characteristics. Two brown-eyed parents may have a blue-eyed child : when this happens the parents may say the child "inherits his eyes from his grandfather", or something of that sort.

But of course there is no direct handing on of *characteristics* from generation to generation, since all characteristics are developed anew in each individual. If one inherits a house, the house itself is actually handed over. This is legal inheritance, and it must be clearly distinguished from biological inheritance. The material passed on to us from our parents, and responsible for biological inheritance, is microscopic : it is contained in an egg-cell (produced by the mother) and a sperm (produced by the father). The two unite, and the fertilised egg so produced develops into the new individual with his or her own particular quota of "characters". The production of sperm and eggs is further described in chapter 4.

7

From the difference in size between egg and sperm it might be thought that the mother must have more effect on a child's characteristics than the father. This is not the case. In general, inherited effects are equal from both parents. There are minor exceptions to this rule, but few have anything to do with the fact that a human egg is about 85,000 times as large as a sperm.

HUMAN CHROMOSOMES

Above, the 24 pairs drawn in a row ; below, as they are seen in a cell during division of a nucleus

THE CHROMOSOMES

The reason for the equal part played by egg and sperm is that each has a complete set of structures called chromosomes, and it is the chromosomes that carry the genetic factors, or *genes*. To appreciate the part played by chromosomes in heredity we must understand something of the microscopic structure of the tissues of the body. If small fragments, or very thin slices, of animal or plant tissues are examined under a microscope they are seen to be divided into exceedingly small compartments, the cells. Tissues grow by the increase in the size of the cells, followed by division of the cells into two. Cells vary a great deal in shape and function, but nearly all have a nucleus. Ordinarily a nucleus is a nearly spherical object without any obvious internal structure, but when a cell divides most of the nuclear material condenses, to form a number of objects resembling minute rods or threads. These are *chromosomes*, and their number varies with the species of animal or plant ; in man there are 48, forming 24 pairs. Each chromosome can be seen, soon after it appears, to be already split along its length ; later the halves of each chromosome separate, and two complete sets, each of 48 chromosomes, are formed. The cell then divides into two, and each newly-formed cell takes one set. However many times cell division takes place each cell has a nucleus made up of the full complement of 24 pairs of chromosomes.

The only important exception to this rule is provided by the germ cells—the egg-cells of the female and the sperm-cells of the male. When the germ cells are produced, in the ovaries and testes respectively, the chromosomes behave differently : each egg or sperm receives only 24 chromosomes, or one of each pair present in an ordinary cell. When an egg is fertilised by a sperm the two half-sets of chromosomes come together, and so in the fertilised egg the full number of 48 is restored.

This is the mechanism by which each parent contributes equally, on the average, to a child's constitution. The expression "on the average" has to be put in because if a single person is studied it often seems that resemblance to one parent is much more marked than to the other. This is not because there has been any abnormality in the chromosome mechanism: it is often because some of the genes carried by the chromosomes of one parent may mask the effects of the corresponding ones on the other set of chromosomes. Examples of how some of these genes operate are given in the next chapter.

The chromosome mechanism ensures that the genetic factors are distributed throughout the body. The fertilised egg is itself a cell, and all the cells of the body are derived from it by a series of repeated divisions. And we have already seen that after division each cell has a full complement of chromosomes. (Plate 1, opposite p. 16; and frontispiece and figure on p. 10.)

If, then, a child has hair similar to that of its parents, it is not because the hair is handed on in any material sense, like a wig, but because the parents' chromosomes, carrying

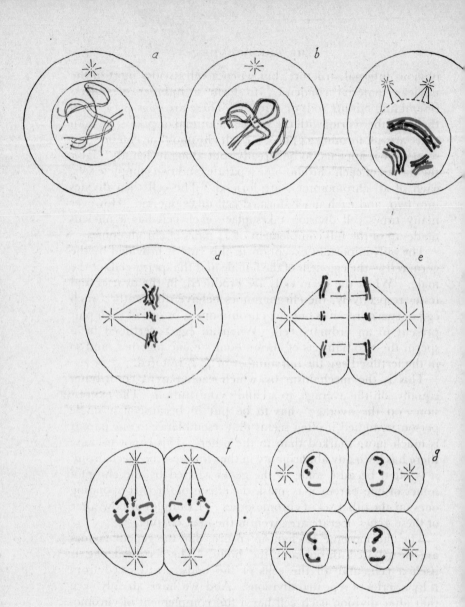

CHROMOSOMES OF EGG AND SPERM

When egg and sperm-cells are formed (in the ovaries and testes respectively) a special type of nuclear division (meiosis) takes place : the result is that the nucleus of an egg or sperm has only 24 chromosomes, instead of 24 pairs. At fertilisation the full number of 48 is restored. Here only 3 pairs are shown. (Compare frontispiece) genetic factors which bring about the development of that particular kind of hair, are passed on, and are present in the cells of the skin from which hair grows. (The example of hair is taken because hair characters are relatively little affected by environment. In general it is of course true that part of our resemblance to our parents is due to sharing a common environment with them : for example, we grow up in the same country, and so learn the same language.)

It can now be seen why in biology the words "heredity" and "inherited" are often avoided. Very often something is said to be "genetically determined"; this means that it is due to the action of the genetic factors, or genes, carried by the chromosomes and transmitted in the way described. The man who invented the term genetics, Francis Galton, preferred to speak of *nature* and *nurture*, instead of heredity and environment.

Now that the machinery of transmission from parent to offspring has been established it is possible to be clear about what the often misused words *familial* and *congenital* signify. A disease is sometimes said to be familial when it occurs in several members of the same family or group of related families. By itself, this tells us nothing about its causes. A familial disease may be largely due to the transmission of a particular gene, or it may be caused by some environmental influence that acts on many members of the family. Tuberculosis, for example, is particularly common among people, such as those of the mining communities of South Wales, who do exhausting work in conditions that encourage its appearance. If several members of the same family get tuberculosis it may be because they all suffer these conditions, or because one infects others. However, there may be a genetic factor *as well*. People vary a great deal in their resistance to tuberculosis, and part of the variation is genetically determined. It follows that there may be families of persons all with a lower resistance than the average, because they all possess a particular set of genes.

This is far from saying that tuberculosis is an "inherited disease". The immediate cause of tuberculosis is infection with a particular kind of microbe, the tubercle bacillus, or T.B., together with a certain degree of susceptibility in the infected person. The infection itself is an environmental effect, arising usually from the presence of the microbe in the air or in milk. But susceptibility is affected both by other environmental influences, such as housing, and by genetic factors.

The word familial thus covers a complex set of possibilities. The same applies to the word congenital. A congenital condition is present in the new-born child. The word thus refers to the time of appearance of the condition, and not to its cause. The cause may be genetical, at least in part, but sometimes it is wholly environmental. For instance, congenital syphilis is due to infection of the child by the mother during its passage from the womb to the outside—a purely "environmental" effect. By contrast, "lobster claw", an abnormality of the hands and feet, appears, as far as we know, in all individuals with a particular rare gene. On the other hand there is a rare condition called Mongolian idiocy which is due to a gene : unless a person has two genes of this particular kind (one from each parent) he cannot be a Mongolian idiot. The condition might consequently be said to be genetically determined. But here there is a complication : not all people with the two genes are Mongolian idiots ; Mongolian idiocy is more likely to appear among the children of relatively old mothers, and especially of those who are over the age of forty when they have a child. (Even among such children it is very rare). It seems therefore that conditions in the womb influence its appearance : in other words the environment of the unborn child also plays a part. So in this instance both genetical and environmental differences are important.

ENVIRONMENT (OR "NURTURE")

It will be evident that the term environment, like heredity, is here being used in a sense rather different from the usual one. Environment is used in this book to refer to every influence that acts on the individual from outside, from conception (or fertilisation) onwards.

The environmental influences that first act on a human being are those of the womb (or uterus). We have just had one example of their importance, and there are plenty of others. The nutrition of the unborn child depends on the food materials carried in the mother's blood. This blood circulates in the tissues of the womb, and some of the materials dissolved in it diffuse into the blood stream of the embryo, which is separated from it only by a very thin membrane. (The belief that the mother's blood flows directly into the blood vessels of the embryo is erroneous.) If the mother herself is receiving a poor diet, the child too will suffer : deficiency of calcium in the mother's food may be responsible for defective bones in the child.

A mother's mental state may also affect an unborn child. It is believed, for instance, that a recent increase in pyloric stenosis in infants reflected the increase in mental strain due to war. Pyloric stenosis is a narrowing of the exit of the stomach, causing vomiting of a peculiar kind and inability to take food normally. It is thought that mental disturbance in a mother causes an alteration in the contents of her blood, and that this in turn affects the blood of the embryo and brings about an abnormal growth of certain tissues.

In this example the mental state of the mother affects the child through a change in her blood, and this change does not give rise to the same mental state in the infant. There is nothing here in common with the belief that what a mother sees or thinks during pregnancy directly affects the appearance or thoughts of the child after it is born. In a novel published shortly before the first world war a child is described as being born "hating his father", as a result of the feelings of his mother towards her husband. A new-born infant could not hate in this fashion, because it lacks a sufficiently developed nervous system. Only later can a child be induced to hate. The influence of the state of mind of a pregnant mother on her child is only through such prosaic matters as the blood supply to the womb. She cannot ensure that her child will have a placid temperament by being calm herself, or that it will appreciate the arts as a result of her visits to picture galleries and concerts during pregnancy.

Once a child is born the environmental influences acting on him become much more complex. His parents form a most important part of the environment, but there are also other people, the climate, food, disease germs in the air and elsewhere and many more subtle influences.

LAMARCK AND LYSENKO

The importance of environmental influences is indeed obvious, and there are plenty of further examples in later chapters. There is however one supposed action of the environment which has caused violent controversy. It is commonly thought that if, let us say, a man becomes by training skilled in a particular trade, his children are likely to inherit some of this acquired skill. (Of course, many children learn their father's trade as they grow up, but learning from one's father is for our present purpose no different from learning from a school teacher : heredity is not involved in any biological sense.)

This doctrine, misleadingly called "the inheritance of acquired characters", is associated with the name of Lamarck, an eighteenth century biologist. And so we sometimes speak of *Lamarckism*. It is a doctrine that has long been in disrepute with biologists, but lately the controversy has been revived in a new form.

According to Lamarck, and to many other biologists of his time and later, various effects operating during the life of an individual influence the character of the individual's offspring : the most important are use and disuse, and Lamarck considered that the will or desire of an organism to perform an act was also important. Lamarck was unusual for his time in being an evolutionist : he was convinced that (as is now generally agreed) species are not immutable, but undergo a slow process of change ; change, he thought, was brought about by the influence of the environment on successive generations, and their efforts to adapt themselves to it. The present theory of evolution is described in chapter 5. Our concern here is with the question whether Lamarckian transmission of environmental effects can be found anywhere, and if so the extent to which it is important.

One of the reasons for doubting the Lamarckian theory is our knowledge of the chromosomes and genes, and of the part they play in heredity. If the theory were true we should have to suppose that a process, such as learning to be a good pianist, caused changes in a person's genes so that children subsequently conceived would be capable of becoming pianists without training, or with less training. There is no known way in which this could occur, and what we know of the ways in which genes change is against it.

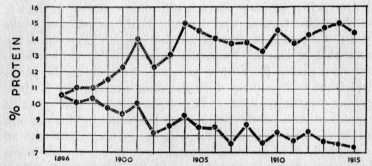

THE EFFECT OF SELECTION OVER MANY GENERATIONS

Maize plants were selected (a) for high protein content of the seed (upper line) and (b) for low protein content. At first, on the whole, selection had a marked effect ; but after 1902 in the low-content strain, and 1904 in the high-content strain, selection had no detectable effect : change from year to year might be slightly up or down, perhaps owing to weather differences. This is an example of selection producing a pure line, in which there is no genetic variability on which further selection can act.

However, the apparently impossible sometimes turns out to be true, and many experiments have been devised to test the theory. Most of these experiments have failed to give acceptable evidence of a Lamarckian effect : the genes seem for the most part to be remarkably stable, and unaffected by ordinary environmental changes. Thus the effect of disuse was tested when flies were bred in the dark for 69 generations ; at the end their eyes were unaffected, and they reacted normally to light. Further, in some experiments it has been possible to show that the Lamarckian effect does not occur where, if the theory were true, it would be expected to do so. The best known of these experiments were on beans. The plants were self-fertilised, and the progeny selected for size of seed. It was found that if, in each generation, the largest seeds are selected for planting, the average size of seed, as might be expected, increases. This process does not, however, continue indefinitely : after a number of generations the *average* size

15

reaches a constant figure—or, if it shows variation, there is no steady trend up or down. And no further selection makes any difference.

On each bean plant there is still some variation in the size of the seeds, because size depends partly on position in the pod : if a seed is in an unfavourable position its growth is less than that of others. Nevertheless, even if the smallest seeds are now chosen for further breeding, the seeds on the plants which grow from them show the same average size as those grown from large seeds. The explanation is that selection combined with self-fertilisation has led to the production of a strain of plants in which there is *no genetical variation* : all individuals have the same genetic constitution, and variation between them, if it is observed, can be due only to environment. Variation in the sizes of the seeds is due to the environmental effect of a different food supply in different positions.

For the Lamarckian theory the importance of these experiments is that here is an environmental effect—position in the pod—which is well-marked in each generation but which has no effect on later generations. However carefully large or small seeds are selected for further breeding the average size of seed on the new plants remains constant. If there were a Lamarckian effect selection of the largest beans would lead to further increase in size in later generations, or of the smallest to a decrease.

A strain of plants or animals, in which breeding has eliminated genetical variation, is called a *pure line*. In animals something very close to a pure line can be got by brother and sister mating for thirty or more generations, and this has often been done with quickly breeding species such as certain flies, and even with rats and mice. Pure lines are of great value for some types of research. If, for instance, the effects on growth of two different diets are to be compared, it is desirable to give the diets to two groups of animals, each as nearly as possible genetically identical : it is then probable that any differences observed between the groups are not genetically determined, and a possible source of error is avoided. Inbred stocks, as we shall see in chapter 11, are also of great importance in agriculture and stockbreeding.

These facts are important also for human biology. If two human groups, such as the inhabitants of Japan and of Scotland, are compared in respect of a character such as height or intelligence, both of which can be measured, the averages may be found to differ. The two groups certainly have different environments, and doubtless also differ genetically. The difficulty is to find out the extent to which environmental and genetic differences influence the observed variation in height or intelligence. In later chapters we shall see that, despite the difficulties, it is possible to reach some conclusions in problems of this kind. It is however essential to realise that the difficulties exist.

If we return now to Lamarckism we can sum up the conventional view of the theory, as it is found in most textbooks, by saying that it is held to be without experimental foundation, and contrary to everything we know of the mechanism of heredity. It is now however realised that this outright rejection, of all transmission of environmental effects, is too sweeping. Although what has been said above is true as far as it goes, there is much more to be said. The criticism of the conventional view is today associated particularly with the work of a Russian biologist, Lysenko. But although his views have received more public notice in the western Press than those of almost any British or American scientist there has been less discussion of the biological issues involved than might be thought.

Lysenko has long been known for his studies of the development of plants from the seed, and in particular for treatments which make it possible for seed to be sown successfully in cold climates. He and his colleagues have also investigated the grafting of fruit trees. In all their work they have been concerned with the urgent problems of raising agricultural yields. They now assert that altering the environment of the growing plant not only influences the growth of the plant itself, but also exerts a persistent effect on the progeny of the plant : for instance, once a winter wheat has been converted to a spring wheat (that is, one that will develop as soon as it is sown without a dormant period in the soil), the wheat plants of subsequent generations retain this character. Another example, from grafting experiments, concerns tomato plants :

it is reported that seeds taken from grafts may grow into plants with some of the characters of the *host* plant—that is, not of the parent plant but of the plant on to which the parent plant had been grafted.

Claims of this sort might seem to conflict with the apparently stable character of the genes referred to earlier, but they are not on that account rejected by geneticists. Similar phenomena have been observed in a number of species beside those studied in the U.S.S.R., and some have been given a tentative explanation. Although most genetical transmission is a function of the chromosomes of the cell nucleus it has long been known that some genetic effects are due to factors outside the nucleus; these factors are passed on in the egg-cell, which has a considerable mass of non-nuclear material (cytoplasm), but not in the sperm. It follows that they are transmitted only by the mother and not by the father. It is held that factors of this sort are more easily influenced by environmental effects, and that they are involved in phenomena such as those of the grafted tomatoes.

This view represents a departure from the simple, conventional scheme based entirely on nuclear inheritance. It does, however, leave the main body of genetical theory intact : the only difference is that some of the phenomena of heredity, probably a very small proportion, are recognised as exceptions which have to be accounted for outside the theory. But this is not the position of Lysenko and his followers : from their studies of environmental action they have concluded that the whole structure of modern genetics is full of errors, and needs to be swept away and replaced with a new one which can account adequately for their experimental results. The question for us now is, to what extent are these criticisms justified ?

Lysenko and his followers do not deny the rôle of the chromosomes in heredity, but they criticise emphasis on the *unchanging* nature of the genes. This criticism follows naturally from their belief that they can alter the genetic characters of organisms by altering their environment. The orthodox view is that genes do change, but only rarely. Examples of such changes, or *mutations*, are given in chapters 3 and 8; the nearest we get to mutation in everyday experience is the occurrence of a "sport" (or *mutant*) in a garden plant : the sudden appearance of an oddity among normal plants may be due to a mutation of some kind. The rate at which mutation occurs can be increased by the use of radiation, such as X-rays : suitable doses directed towards the egg-cells of fruit-flies, for instance, have greatly increased the number of abnormal types in later generations ; and these abnormalities are inherited. (If atomic bombs were ever used again in war a similar effect would probably be observed in human populations.) The abnormalities are of the same kinds as those observed in untreated flies, but they are much more numerous. Mutations have been induced in plants also by chemical treatment, and sometimes the mutant forms produce larger fruit and so are useful ; these chemically induced mutations involve, not one gene, but the whole set of chromosomes.

The claims of the Lysenko school of biologists go further : according to them particular inheritable changes can be induced by special treatment, and in this way new types of plants and animals, useful to agriculture, can be deliberately created. They hold further that this type of research has been held up by conventional genetics, which has made little contribution to agricultural practice. The last statement is certainly true : there are only a few examples of conventional genetics aiding in the breeding of new and useful crop plants or domestic animals, and much of the practical breeding that is done would be just as effective without it. It does not, however, follow that genetical theories are false. If we examine serious comment on this subject we find that opinion ranges between two extremes : on the one hand are those who hold that, while agricultural yields in the Soviet Union have admittedly been increased, the new theories are nonsense and Lysenko himself is a charlatan ; at the other extreme it has been suggested that there is due in biological theory a great new development, such as occurs at unpredictable intervals in all the sciences, and that Lysenko is its herald.

There is no doubt that controversy will continue, and little doubt that new knowledge will rapidly accumulate. The connexion between the agents of heredity and the processes of development from egg-cell to adult is one of the central topics of biology, as well as one of the most difficult. Further study will certainly yield results of both practical and theoretical interest. We must await these results with patience.

TWINS AND HEREDITY

There remains a good deal more, of a less controversial kind, to say on the subject of disentangling the effects of nature and nurture. One of the great problems, as we have seen, is to determine *how much* variation in a given character, such as stature, is due to heredity, and how much to environment. There are certain human beings who provide us with a special opportunity for answering such questions. They are the so-called identical twins.

Human twins are of two kinds. About three pairs in every four are the result of the presence, when insemination occurs, of two egg-cells instead of only one. Both are fertilised, and they grow side-by-side in the womb. Small mammals such as cats, dogs, rats and rabbits, and some larger ones such as pigs, lions and tigers, produce several young at a birth in this way. Human twins of this sort are called binovular, or two-egg, twins, and they can be and often are very different from each other ; they may of course differ in sex. Twins of the other type develop from a single fertilised egg which gives rise to two separate individuals. Twins of this sort are genetically identical : since they both originate from the same fertilised egg-cell, the chromosomes in the nuclei of the cells in all parts of their bodies are derived from the single set of chromosomes originally present in that egg. Such twins often show remarkable resemblances, not only in appearance but also in emotional and intellectual characteristics. They are always of the same sex.

But the important fact about them is that they are never quite identical. Most are brought up together, and so have very similar environments as well as identical genetical factors. Nevertheless, even then, differences can be detected, though they are much less than those between ordinary brothers or sisters, or between binovular twins. For example, they differ in their scores in intelligence tests, on the average, by about 9 points. Ordinary brothers and sisters show an average difference of about 16 points.

More interesting are the pairs that have been separated early, and brought up by different guardians and in very different conditions. It is common to hear of such pairs that they remain remarkably similar. Often, this is true : there are instances of separated pairs being reunited as adults, as a result of one being mistaken for the other. It is also true that similarity between uniovular twins, whether separated or not, extends to the most extraordinary details : for instance the distribution of decay in the teeth is often the same. Sometimes the similarity is of medical importance. One of a pair of uniovular twins living in Oxford died of an inoperable cancer of the stomach. The survivor was X-rayed, but no trouble could be detected. X-raying was repeated at three-monthly intervals, and after a year there appeared a slight indication of a growth in the stomach wall. The surgeon consulted held that the X-ray evidence alone was insufficient to justify operation, but he operated nevertheless, and duly removed a very early cancer of the type of which the first twin had died. The patient recovered.

To return to the pairs that have been separated in infancy, we do not invariably find that they are strikingly similar. One pair of boys, born in Glasgow, was separated at 3 years : one remained in a working-class quarter of the city, the other went to live in a village outside Glasgow. At 16, when they were compared, it was found that both were above the average in their score in intelligence tests, but that the city child scored 125 to the other's 106. Both were good at football, but the country-bred one was physically superior ; in particular, he was an inch taller ; he also showed more mechanical ability.

Cases like this illustrate how environment can affect both intellectual achievement and physical development. Even more marked emotional differences are sometimes shown. Two American girls, uniovular twins, were separated in infancy. One lived with a comfortable middle-class family with many social contacts and able to provide a good education. The other was looked after by a couple in poor circumstances, and the general education she received was not so good. At twenty the first girl was a cheerful, sociable individual, clearly enjoying life and without any evident psychological difficulties.

21

3

The other was moody, shy, diffident and depressed, and spoke with a lisp.

THE INTERACTION OF NATURE AND NURTURE

It is sometimes asked : which is the more important, heredity or environment ? There is no simple answer to this question. If the question means, which has the greater *effect* ? no general answer is possible, but only a number of particular answers. For instance, individual differences in eye-colour are mainly determined genetically, and so for this particular characteristic heredity may be said to be the more important. At the other extreme infection with measles, for example, is mainly dependent on the presence in the environment of a sufficiently heavy concentration of the germs that cause measles.

Between the two extremes come characters such as height. There is no doubt that heredity plays a part in determining a person's height : if you have tall parents you are *more likely* to be tall than short. On the other hand, growth is certainly affected by environmental influences such as nutrition. In England, before 1940, boys who went to schools at which heavy fees were charged ("public" schools) were on the average about four inches taller than the children of the poorer parents who could afford to send their children only to free schools. This by itself proves nothing : the poor might conceivably be genetically incapable of growing to the stature of the rich. (In chapter 8 we shall see that some people have believed that this sort of genetic difference exists.) However, experiment has also shown that if the children of the poor receive a diet more like that of the more fortunate children, they approach more and more closely to them in height and weight. This effect was observed on a very large scale during the second world war, when rationing and price control made possible a great improvement in the food eaten by most people in Britain. The height of any one person is, then, an expression of the combined effects of his genetic make-up and his environment. We cannot say that one has a greater effect than the other. This interaction of nature and nurture has often been illustrated by experiments on animals. It is possible to isolate pure strains of mice with different capacities for growth. When this is done it is found that different strains grow best in different conditions : there is no single environment that is best for all kinds of mice. We can reasonably suspect that the same applies to man. So the adage that one man's meat is another's poison expresses a very general and important biological principle.

Despite these facts there are still those who attach more weight to nature than to nurture, and others who insist that nurture is all-important. Those who put the emphasis on nature, or heredity, we shall mention again, in chapter 8. Meanwhile it is as well to consider what is meant by those who lay especial emphasis on environment. So far, in answer to the question : which is the more important? we have given only the sort of non-committal and rather irritating response that often comes from the scientist. Neither nature nor nurture, we have said, can reasonably be regarded as having a greater effect than the other.

But it is possible to improve on this answer. If the question is considered from a practical point of view, from the point of view of getting something useful achieved, then the answer must put the emphasis on environment. This, of course, applies only when man is being considered. We can, and do, improve our livestock and our cultivated plants by breeding : in doing so we may kill the young that do not please us, permit only a selected few to breed, and perhaps derive much of our stock from artificial insemination or hand pollination. But in man selective breeding of this sort is rarely proposed. We must, with a few possible minor exceptions, accept the genetic constitutions of existing populations, and try to adjust the environment to them. If coal miners dislike coal mining, and if they are also liable to get serious diseases in the pursuit of their calling, there is no question of breeding a strain of men that will react differently. The problem is to alter the conditions of coal mining. Later chapters will provide much more evidence in support of this conclusion.

CHAPTER 3

MENDELISM AND MAN

ALTHOUGH we can do nothing to alter our own genetic constitutions, and though few of us would alter our plans for marriage on genetic grounds, it is nevertheless worth while to know all we can about human genetics. The principles of genetics have mostly been worked out from experiments on plants that can be artificially pollinated, and on quickly breeding animals, such as the famous fruit fly, *Drosophila*. The first man to publish an accurate account of the way in which what we now call genes determine the transmission of characters was an Austrian priest, Gregor Mendel. Mendel used sweet peas for his experiments. It is an extraordinary fact that, although the journal in which he published was available in London and other centres in 1866, it was completely ignored.

In 1900 two Germans, Correns and Tschermak, and a Dutchman, de Vries, independently published papers confirming Mendel's observations. Since then an enormous mass of research has been done on the subject, but Mendel's priority is still acknowledged in the name "Mendelism".

MENDELIAN HEREDITY AND CHROMOSOMES

It is possible to give examples of "Mendelian heredity" from man. Let us suppose that a woman with bright red hair marries a man with non-red hair (the precise shade of the man's hair does not matter) ; and that all their offspring have non-red hair. (This will happen if the man is not carrying a single gene for red hair : in other words if he is, as an animal breeder would say, pure bred for non-red hair). The non-red haired state thus masks red hair, and is referred to as *dominant* to red hair ; red hair is said to be *recessive*. Let us now suppose that one of the children of this couple marries the child of a similar couple, and that they in turn have a large family : say twelve children. Although they themselves have non-red hair, one in four of their children, on the average, will have red hair : that is, the most probable number of red-haired children out of twelve will be three.

Characteristics are sometimes said to skip a generation, and this is an example. The next question is : what is the explanation ? In the previous chapter we saw that every individual receives one set of chromosomes from each parent ; the chromosomes are themselves the bearers of the genetic factors, the genes. Bright red hair depends on the presence of a gene which we may represent as **r**, and red hair occurs only in individuals (of either sex) who have received **r** from both parents. Red-haired people therefore have the constitution **rr**. In the case described above the woman in the first couple was of this constitution. Her husband, on the other hand, had no **r** gene. In him, the corresponding genes were for non-red hair, and his constitution may be represented as **RR**. Capital letters indicate dominance.

Each of the children of this couple received **r** from the mother and **R** from the father. Their constitution was thus **Rr**, and their hair non-red, since **R** always causes non-red hair even if **r** is present. The next step was the marriage of two persons with the constitution **Rr**. Their children may be **RR, Rr** or **rr**, and the average proportions of non-red to red will be 3:1. This three to one ratio is of course observable only if large numbers are studied : it cannot be established from observation of one or two families, even if they are exceptionally large. In fact, as we have already seen, ratios of this kind were first worked out on plants, and then on insects, before they were demonstrated in man. To observe a Mendelian effect it is necessary to breed plants or animals for two generations, and to study the proportions in which the characters occur in large numbers of individuals. By no means all characteristics are inherited in this simple fashion, and the early workers had to hit on ones that are.

One of the results of the new genetics was that it showed that heredity is not a blending process. In the past it had been thought that each individual was a blend of the characteristics of his parents, just as orange-coloured paint can be made by blending yellow and red. In the example of hair-colour we see that red hair appears in undiluted form in the second generation. We therefore attribute its appearance to genes that are transmitted intact from generation to generation.

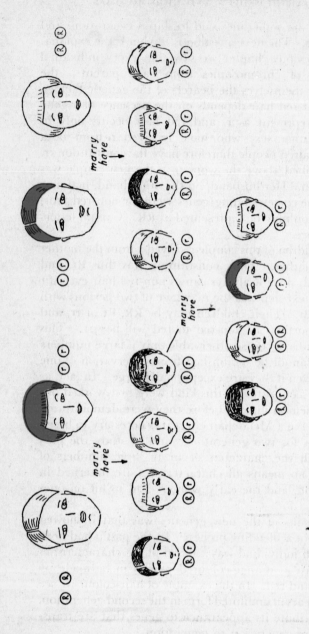

INHERITANCE OF RED HAIR IN MAN

Bright red hair is due to a recessive gene, that is, one of which the effect is seen only if it is present with another gene of the same kind. This simple example shows how children can have characteristics which neither parent has. It illustrates also the fact that heredity is not a blending process, like mixing paints, but that the inherited factors (the genes) keep their identity from generation to

R · gene for non-red hair
(a dominant gene)
r · gene for red hair

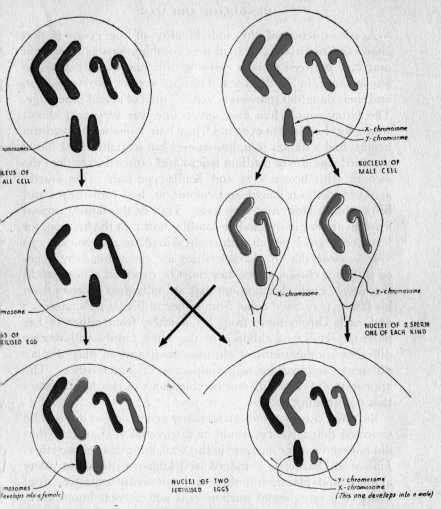

Chromosomes

NUCLEUS OF
MALE CELL

X-chromosome
Y-chromosome

NUCLEUS OF
MALE CELL

Chromosome

Chromosomes
of
Fertilised egg

X-chromosome

Y-chromosome

NUCLEI OF 2 SPERM
ONE OF EACH KIND

Chromosomes
(develops into a female)

NUCLEI OF TWO
FERTILISED EGGS

Y-chromosome
X-chromosome
(This one develops into a male)

SEX DETERMINATION

Sex is determined at the moment of fertilisation, and depends on the sperm. There are two kinds of sperm : one kind has an X-chromosome, the other a Y-chromosome which has very few genes. Each egg-cell has one X-chromosome. Eggs fertilised with the first type of sperm have two X-chromosomes and become females ; thus all the body-cells of females have two X-chromosomes. Eggs fertilised with sperm containing a Y-chromosome have the constitution XY, and become males. Certain genes, such as the one causing hæmophilia, are on the X-chromosome and are said to be *sex-linked* (see next figure)

27

A consequence of this individuality of the genes is that characteristics may appear in new combinations as a result of marriage between persons carrying different sets of genes. In one instance, in South Africa, a Griqua woman married a Scot, and their daughter married a "white" man of mixed parentage. The latter couple had four sons : one was very tall, almost white, but had brown eyes and frizzy hair ; one was of medium height, had a darker skin, brown eyes but straight, black hair ; the third was also of medium height and rather darker than the second, with brown eyes and Kaffir-type hair ; the fourth, again of medium height and coloration, had brown eyes and brown-black Hottentot-type hair. Thus in this family various features appear in unfamiliar combination : in the first son, for instance, negro-type hair with a light skin (Plate 2, opposite p. 17.)

It is clear that if characteristics are determined by genes on different chromosomes they must be expected to *segregate* in this way. Each chromosome that an individual receives from his father may have come from either of his father's parents ; and each chromosome from his mother, from either of her parents. Different children of the same family will receive different combinations of chromosomes, and so may display different combinations of grandparental characteristics. The appearance of these different combinations of characters shows that no blending occurs.

But each chromosome carries many genes, and so it might be expected that instances would be discovered of characters that did not segregate or separate in this way, but remained together. *Linkage* of characters is indeed well known to occur in many animals and plants, but there are not many examples from man. For our present purpose it is not of great importance, since linkage is very rarely complete. The reason for the failure of linkage is shown in the diagram on page 10: the cause of it is an exchange of material between pairs of chromosomes during the formation of the eggs and sperm. This exchange of material inevitably breaks the linkage between genes on the chromosomes.

The general conclusion then is that genetic effects are determined by individual particles, the genes, and that the genes may appear in any combination in different individuals.

This recombination is the origin of much of the variation between people that we see around us. Even a group of people living in a small community and with very similar environments may show great variation in appearance and in other characters. Though part of the variation may be due to small environmental differences, a great deal comes from the mixing and reshuffling of the genes in each generation.

SEX DETERMINATION

One of the most obvious of the characteristics that can be said to be inherited, is sex. It is true that environmental agencies can interfere with the development of sex characteristics : in some mammals the presence of a twin of opposite sex in the womb may cause the development of a mixture of male and female organs ; in other words, the production of an intersex. But this, though it exemplifies once again the intermingling of the effects of heredity and environment, is not of significance for our present purpose.

In normal development sex is determined by the chromosomes by a simple mechanism. We have already seen that there are twenty-four pairs of chromosomes in man. One pair plays a special part in sex determination. In a woman's cells the members of this pair are identical, as far as can be seen with a microscope ; both are called X-chromosomes. In a man's cells there is only one X-chromosome ; with it is a smaller one, the Y-chromosome. Now consider what happens when the germ-cells are produced, each with a half-set of chromosomes. Each egg-cell gets one X-chromosome, but a sperm-cell may have either an X-chromosome or a Y. There are consequently two kinds of sperm. If an egg is fertilised by a sperm with an X-chromosome the fertilised egg (with its full set of chromosomes) will have two X-chromosomes and will develop into a female ; but if a Y-bearing sperm fertilises it there will be one X and one Y and so development will be into a male.

One of the first questions arising from this is : can we control sex in man, or in other animals, by allowing only X-bearing, or only Y-bearing, sperm to reach the egg ? At present, in 1949, the answer is, no ; attempts have been made but so far none has been entirely successful. It is, however, possible that in normal conditions the Y-bearing sperm have a better chance of fertilising an egg than those with an X-chromosome. It is well known that rather more boys are born than girls : in Britain about 105 boys are born for every 100 girls. This is what is meant when it is said that the sex ratio at birth is 105. We do not know what the sex ratio is at conception ; it has been said that more male fœtuses die than female, but recent work suggests that this is not the case. It is however certain that more males are conceived than females. This is not what would be expected from a knowledge of the sex determining mechanism : female-producing sperm (X) and male-producing sperm (Y) are produced in equal numbers, and if the two types have equal chances of successful fertilisation the sex ratio at conception should be 100. The fact that it is higher suggests that Y-bearing sperm have an advantage.

It is clear that the possibility of different behaviour by the two types of sperm is important. Quite apart from the control of sex in man it would be of great value if it could be arranged that the great majority of calves born in dairy herds were female; similarly, on poultry farms, it would be an advantage if most chicks hatched were female. Artificial insemination is already well-established. It is possible that eventually it will be possible to treat sperm, collected for artificial insemination, so that only one kind of sperm remains active.

It is a remarkable fact that the high initial sex ratio, combined with the higher mortality among males, gives a sex ratio of about 100 at puberty : youths of each sex are in approximately equal numbers. But in advanced countries the lower death rate among women continues, and at 85 the sex ratio is about 55 : nearly two women to each man. The greater survival of women is not fully understood; occupational hazards play some part in it, but it may be directly related to the possession of two X-chromosomes. The Y-chromosome is almost inactive genetically : it carries hardly any genes. It follows that if the one X-chromosome of a man carries recessive, disadvantageous genes these genes will be able to exert their disadvantageous effects ; whereas in a woman the second X-chromosome may carry corresponding genes that do not confer a disadvantage :

30

these "normal" genes will mask the effects of recessives. It is well established that recessive genes which reduce the chances of survival exist in other animals, and no doubt they occur also in man.

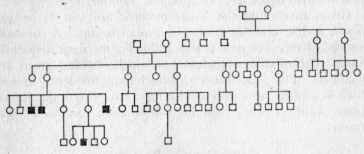

□ NORMAL MALE   ▨ HAEMOPHILIC MALE   O FEMALE

HÆMOPHILIA

Pedigree illustrating origin by mutation, or sudden change, in a normal gene, occurring in a family with no previous history of haemophilia

One gene, carried on the X-chromosome, is indeed already known to confer a very serious disadvantage. This is the gene responsible for the disease hæmophilia, in which the blood clots only very slowly, if at all. Hæmophilics have a very low expectation of life, since they may bleed to death from a small cut, or through internal hæmorrhage. Hæmophilia is known only in males. The gene responsible is recessive, and a man gets the disease as a result of receiving from his mother an X-chromosome which carries the gene. The mother, having another X-chromosome carrying a dominant gene which enables blood to clot in the normal way, is not a hæmophilic. Thus hæmophilia is almost always transmitted by a normal woman carrying, unknown to herself, a gene that is likely to kill half of her sons. Only half the sons, on the average, will be affected; the others will have received the other, normal X-chromosome. Theoretically a woman could have two hæmophilia genes, and so have the disease. No such cases are known, perhaps because the possession of the two genes prevents development altogether.

One of the women known to have been carriers of hæmo-philia was Queen Victoria of England: one of her sons, at

31

least three grandsons and six great-grandsons have been hæmophilics, including members of the ruling families of Spain and Czarist Russia ; but the members of the present British royal house have escaped the offending gene.

Genes carried on the X-chromosome are said to be *sex-linked*, and several are known in human beings. A common sex-linked recessive gene is responsible for the most frequently found type of colour-blindness, in which red and green are confused. This condition occurs much more frequently in men than in women, because a woman must have two of the appropriate kind of gene, and this combination can occur only rarely.

MENDELISM IN PRACTICE

The obvious places for attempting the application of Mendelian genetics are the farm and the garden. In man there is less scope, but it has nevertheless some potential importance. Sometimes a man or woman about to marry wishes to know whether there is danger that children of the marriage will display some undesirable characteristic. In the previous chapter we saw, for example, that both tuberculosis and at least some types of cancer are influenced by genetic constitution. But with both diseases the genetic effect is too small to be taken into account when marriage is considered. If, for instance, a near relative has died of one of these diseases, that is not a reason for avoiding marriage.

Some diseases, however, are determined genetically in a quite straightforward way. Hæmophilia, as we have seen, is one example, and others are given in chapter 8. There is, in fact, a considerable mass of knowledge on the genetics of human defects, and an authority on human genetics can occasionally give useful information to couples who wish to have children. It is, however, not possible to give this information in a short, non-technical book.

A special case is that of marriage between cousins. The effects of cousin marriage can be considered from the point of view of the individual, or of the community. The individual wishes to know what is the chance of producing defective children. It is impossible to answer this for particular cases :

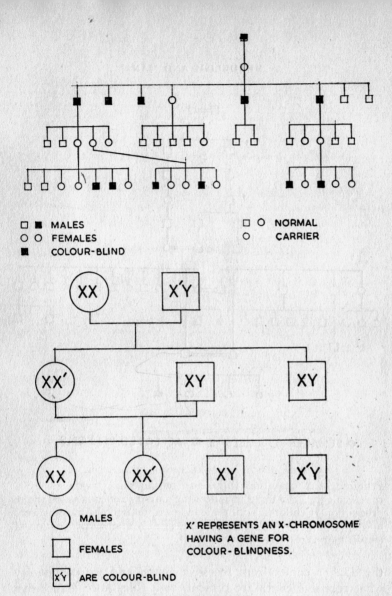

□ ■ MALES	□ ○ NORMAL
○ ○ FEMALES	○ CARRIER
■ COLOUR-BLIND	

MALES

FEMALES

X'Y ARE COLOUR-BLIND

X' REPRESENTS AN X-CHROMOSOME
HAVING A GENE FOR
COLOUR-BLINDNESS.

SEX-LINKED INHERITANCE

Above, pedigree of one type of colour-blindness (red blindness), due to a sex-linked gene. Below, diagram showing how such a gene is transmitted. The effects of a sex-linked gene are shown more often in males than females : in females the presence of a normal gene in one of the X-chromosomes will mask the effect of the recessive mutant gene in the other. In a male there is no second X-chromosome and there can be no masking

33

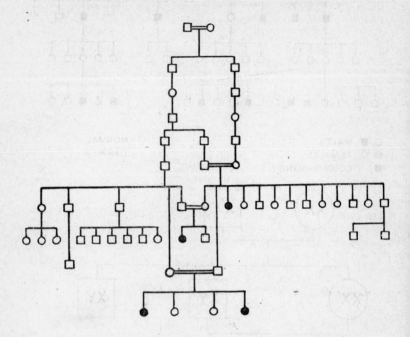

O FEMALES □ MALES ■ ● AFFECTED PERSONS

TRANSMISSION OF A RECESSIVE CHARACTER

Pedigree of a condition (blistering of the skin) produced by a recessive gene. In three instances the marriage of cousins led to the production of children with the condition, though the parents were normal. (This sort of thing happens in only a small proportion of cousin marriages : see text)

the danger comes from recessive genes, and we cannot say what recessive genes are present, as a rule, since a recessive gene exerts (by definition) no effect unless it is present in company with another, similar gene. If both cousins carry the same recessive gene for a particular defect, then it is most likely that the proportion of their children showing the defect will be one in four, or 25 per cent.

It must be emphasised that the great majority of cousin marriages do not produce defective children at all. However, there are recessive genes in man that cause the development of defects ; and two first cousins are more likely both to carry the same recessive genes than two individuals taken at random from the population ; it follows that the chance of two first cousins having defective children is slightly higher than that of an unrelated pair.

This fact does not, and need not, deter first cousins from marrying. The exceptions are cousins with relations who have developed any of the defects known to be determined by recessive genes : these include a fatal skin disease called xeroderma pigmentosum, a form of idiocy (juvenile amaurotic) and a form of deaf mutism ; all are rare diseases.

On the other hand, from the point of view of the community, it can be claimed that cousin marriage is undesirable. If the marriage of first cousins ceased there would be a fall in the incidence of the three conditions just mentioned : this is because, although only a small proportion of cousin marriages produce them, the number so produced is large relative to the total number of sufferers. However, the total genetic effect of forbidding cousin marriages would be quite trivial, and it would be difficult to justify the consequent interference with individual happiness.

Cousin marriage is one form of inbreeding. The most intense form is pairing between parent and offspring, or between sibs (that is, brothers and sisters). Such inbreeding is of great value in plant and animal husbandry, but it is forbidden in most human communities.

Close inbreeding was customary among the rulers of Egypt during a period in the second millenium B.C., and some of the Pharaohs born of marriages between sibs seem to have been persons of very great gifts. Perhaps the Pharaohs of the 18th dynasty were exceptionally free from deleterious recessives.

Ordinarily, however, the danger of producing defective children is a good deal greater from consanguineous marriage than from marriage of first cousins. Apart from obvious defect, there is evidence that close inbreeding in man may lead to lowered fertility.

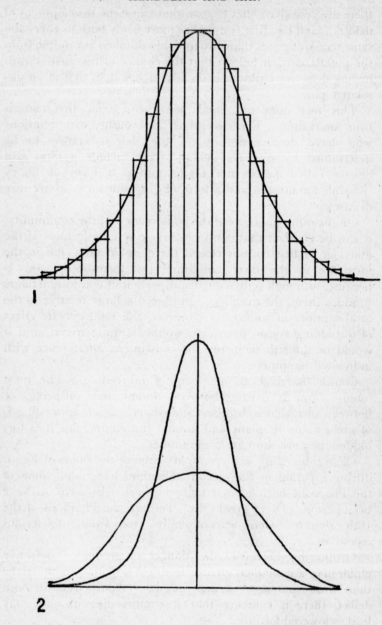

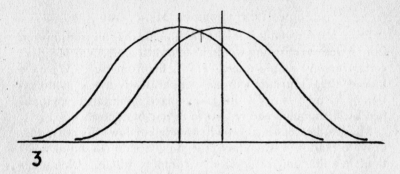

3

CURVES ILLUSTRATING VARIABILITY IN A MEASURABLE CHARACTER

If the height is taken of every person in, say, a large city, the number of persons at each height, to the nearest inch, can be shown by a series of rectangles, as in the first figure. The heights with the greatest number of people would be, perhaps, 5 ft. 5 ins. and 5 ft. 6 ins., and the numbers fall off progressively towards very tall and very short. The smooth curve in the first figure is another way of representing the same facts ; such a curve, when perfectly symmetrical, is called the *curve of normal distribution*. When we study genetical variation which is due to *differences in many genes*, and not just one or two, this is the sort of variation we find ; instead of people being either tall, or short, with no intermediates, we find all heights from very tall to very short, with most people somewhere in the middle.

When two large groups of people are compared in regard to any measurable character, such as strength or fertility or mathematical ability, the two distribution curves may differ both in shape and in the position of the highest point. The second and third figures are simple examples of such differences. An actual instance is given in the figure on page 128.

One of the most important things about comparisons of this kind is that they illustrate that great overlaps can occur, even when averages are different. Many examples of this sort of thing are given in later chapters. For instance, it *may* be true that women, on the average, are genetically inferior to men in mathematical ability, but it does not follow that no women can excel at mathematics, and in fact some do. In some instances, as Haldane has pointed out, we know nothing about average differences, but know only the performances of champions. For example, negroes excel at sprinting, and Finns at long-distance running ; nevertheless other countries sometimes produce champions in both. See the next section

4

Some Limitations of Mendelism

From the foregoing it might be thought that all transmission from parent to offspring would be found to conform to Mendel's comparatively simple rules. This is far from true. We have indeed already mentioned one comparatively minor modification of Mendel's laws : this is sex-linked inheritance, exemplified by hæmophilia and red-green colour-blindness.

Many other cases to which Mendelian laws do not apply provide examples of the fact that the genes do not act in isolation, but function as parts of a complex whole. Characters such as height and weight, which show "continuous variation", are influenced, not by one or two genes only, with the rest neutral in their effects, but by many. In most adult human populations every height, to the nearest one-twentieth of an inch or smaller, is represented, between something less than five feet and something more than six. Of course, a good deal of this variation (as we saw in chapter 2) reflects differences of environment. But insofar as it is genetically determined, the genes responsible are probably to be numbered in hundreds, and each one has only a small effect.

This sort of thing is very important when characters such as "intelligence" are considered. Although there is a correlation between the degree of intelligence shown by parents and children (even when the children are separated from their parents) there is no simple transmission of intelligence, however the latter is measured or defined, as there is of red hair. This, however, is too big a subject for a small book. Those who wish to read a non-technical account of what is known of the genetics of human characteristics should refer to Scheinfeld's *You and Heredity*. They will find that it is still impossible to make valid predictions about the physical or mental abilities of their children.

Mutation

The most drastic exceptions to Mendel's laws are still to be described. So far in this chapter genes have been treated as fixed. This is quite justifiable for many purposes, and their normal constancy from generation to generation was mentioned in chapter 2. But sometimes, as we have seen, they change, or mutate : it appears that, on occasion, during nuclear division, a gene is not reproduced exactly, and the new gene is similar to the old but not identical with it. Thus the gene that causes hæmophilia may be regarded as an inexact copy of a normal gene that enables blood to clot at a normal rate.

The rate of mutation in nature is always very low. It has been calculated that the hæmophilia mutation occurs at a rate of one in 50,000, and this is probably an exceptionally high rate. Hence mutation rarely interferes with genetical experiments. Nevertheless mutation is very important. If genes were absolutely fixed there would be only a limited (though large) number of possible genetic constitutions : beyond these, no new types could be produced, and the evolution of animals and plants could not take place.

CHAPTER 4

FROM EGG TO ADULT

O why did God,
Creator wise, that peopl'd highest Heav'n
With Spirits Masculine, create at last
This noveltie on Earth, this fair defect
Of Nature, and not fill the World at once
With Men as Angels without Feminine,
Or find some other way to generate
Mankind ?

JOHN MILTON

THE study of heredity is perforce a study for the most part of "characters", such as stature or musical ability, and it is easy to think of these characters mechanically, as if they were unchanging units. Actually, as we have seen, everything about us is a product of development : the genes exert their influence, tempered by that of the environment, on *processes*, and the processes go on throughout life at different rates, most of them especially rapidly in early development. We know rather little of the chemical actions by which the genes influence particular processes, such as growth, and nothing which is worth putting in this book. But there is plenty of useful information on the stages of human development and the bodily machinery concerned in reproduction. In this chapter therefore we turn aside from the main theme of human diversity (to which we shall return in the next chapter), to discuss some of the aspects of reproduction and development which are important for a general study of human biology.

SPERM AND EGG

In some mammals sperm are produced during only one part of the year, the rutting season, and only at this time does the male display interest in the female ; but in a man the production of sperm is continuous, and if there is any seasonal variation it is not of practical significance.

A special feature of the testes of most mammals is their presence in a sac of skin, the scrotum, outside the cavity of the abdomen. When there is a breeding season they may descend into the scrotum from the abdomen only during this period. In this position the testes are kept at a temperature several degrees lower than that of the inside of the body, since they have only a thin skin, with no fatty layer such as occurs elsewhere, between them and the air. If the temperature of the scrotum is experimentally raised the sperm produced are ineffective, and temporary sterility may result. In man the application of hot water to the scrotum can have this effect, and it has been suggested that taking hot baths at night may reduce fertility ; there is however no evidence that this possibility is actually realised to any important extent.

Egg-production however is carried on successfully within the abdomen, in the two ovaries. In all mammals eggs are produced intermittently : some produce them only in spring, others at regular intervals throughout most or all of the year. In those that have litters several eggs ripen at once, some coming from each ovary. A woman is usually fertile between the ages of 15 and 45, though exceptionally the fertile period may be much longer. During this period one egg develops every 28 days, approximately, in alternate ovaries, except during pregnancy (and to some extent lactation) when no eggs ripen. A few women produce more than one egg at a time and so, as we saw in chapter 2, may give birth to two or more children at once. An advantage in producing only one child at each birth is that a human child has a long period of slow development, during which parental care is vitally important, and parental care would probably be less effective if several young were born together.

The Menstrual Cycle

The childbearing period in a woman is marked by the "monthly period" : at fairly regular intervals there is a loss of blood and other matter from the vagina lasting for about four days ; the commonest interval between the beginning of one "period" and the beginning of the next is 28 days. The correct name for this event is menstruation. What is the connexion between menstruation and the monthly ripening of an egg-cell ? The answer to this is complex, and, before giving it, it will be

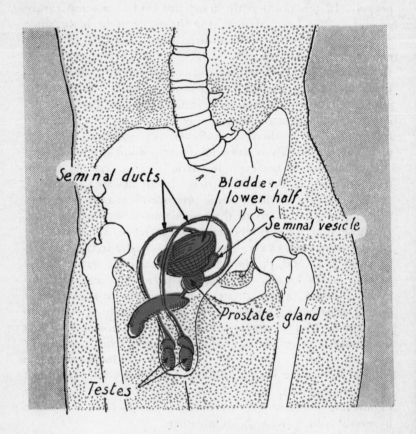

Seminal ducts

Bladder
lower half

Seminal vesicle

Prostate gland

Testes

MALE REPRODUCTIVE ORGANS

The relations with the bladder and with neighbouring parts of the skeleton are shown. Sperm are produced in the testis, and pass along the sperm ducts which join to form the urethra—the tube which carries both sperm and urine through the penis to the outside. The two seminal vesicles (only one shown) are branches of the sperm ducts, and they store sperm. The prostate is one of the glands of which the secretions make up the seminal fluid in which the sperm are suspended

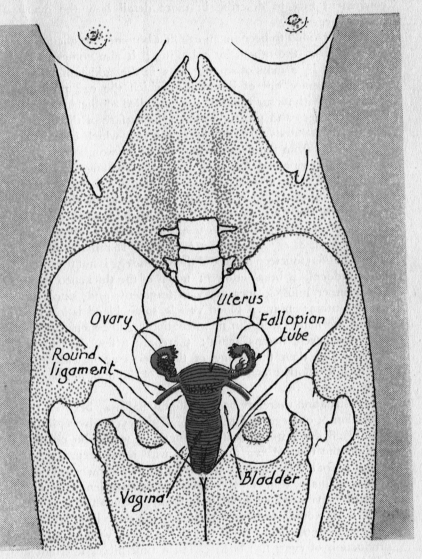

FEMALE REPRODUCTIVE ORGANS IN RELATION TO THE REST OF THE
BODY

The round ligament holds the uterus, or womb, in place. Look also
at the diagram on p. 51

convenient first to describe in more detail how the ovary produces eggs.

A cell destined to become an egg first becomes conspicuously different from the others by enlarging ; it also comes to be surrounded by a mass of smaller cells, in the midst of which appears a space full of liquid into which the egg projects. The space, with its surrounding cells, is called a follicle, and the follicle enlarges and protrudes on to the surface of the ovary. Eventually it bursts and discharges the egg, which enters the tube leading from the ovary to the uterus (or womb).

While this ripening has been going on a change has been taking place in the uterus. The inner lining grows thicker, and its blood supply is increased by enlargement of the blood vessels. By the time the egg is liberated the growth is completed and *the wall of the uterus is now in a state in which it can receive a fertilised egg and allow it to develop*. It remains in this state for about fourteen days, and then, if the egg is not fertilised, quite suddenly it breaks down : much of the thickened tissue of the inner lining comes away in fragments and, since this tissue contains enlarged blood vessels, some blood is lost too. This is the material lost in menstruation. After menstruation the whole cycle begins again : there are a few days of inactivity and then the lining of the uterus again enlarges ; meanwhile another egg (in the ovary of the opposite side) is ripening.

Menstruation therefore occurs roughly half way between the liberation of one egg and the next. If the cycle always lasted exactly 28 days, its most usual length, it would be possible to date the time of egg production with some accuracy : it would probably be 14 days after the first day of menstruation. However, many women have cycles of average length as low as twenty-five days or as high as thirty. Moreover it is not usual for a woman to have consistently the same interval from one period to the next. So although the ovary, with its regular production of eggs, has been called a time-piece, it is not a reliable one. This is of practical importance, both to couples who wish to make sure of having a child and to those who wish to avoid one. Coitus can lead to pregnancy only if a ripe egg-cell is available. We do not know exactly how long the unfertilised human egg survives, but in the rabbit the time is about six hours. Rabbit sperm last about thirty hours. The figures for human eggs and sperms may well be different, but it has been shown that coitus is most likely to cause pregnancy if it takes place about half way between menstruations. This fact is the basis of the "safe-period" method of contraception. Some people, especially Catholics, are adjured on religious grounds not to use any of the efficient contraceptive methods, but are not prevented from avoiding coitus at the time when the woman is presumed to be most fertile. Unfortunately the "safe" periods are by no means wholly safe, since instances are known where coitus just before or just after menstruation was followed by conception. However, if only the two periods of seven days immediately before and after menstruation are used, the chances of conception are materially reduced, and so this is a real method of family limitation. A disadvantage is that many women enjoy coitus most in the middle period, when it is not "safe" at all.

An interesting question is, what is the function of the menstrual cycle ? All mammals have a cycle of some sort : what use is it ? A partial answer to this can be given for most mammals. Eggs are produced only intermittently, sometimes seasonally, and the uterus must be enlarged to receive them ; at the time when eggs and uterus are ready the behaviour of the female changes : she is said to be *on heat*, or *in œstrus*, and she is willing to receive the male. At other times the male is repelled, and coitus is impossible. It is said that the only animals in which rape, or coitus with an unwilling female, is known, are human beings and white mice. (It will be noticed that heat, or œstrus, in other animals does *not* correspond to menstruation in a woman, but to the time when an egg is liberated). It seems that while in most mammals the cycle—the œstrous cycle as it is called—synchronises the activities of the male with the internal changes in the female, in the human species it has lost this function. Nevertheless the cycle remains, though in altered form.

While most mammals have an œstrous cycle, only a few menstruate : they are certain monkeys, the apes, and ourselves. A few others, including the bitch, have a show of blood at certain times, but this is not due to breakdown of the inner lining of the uterus. It is possible that this breakdown, in its early stages, is part of the preparation of the uterus for the embryo which is to develop in it. If there is no fertilised egg, and so no embryo, the breakdown goes on unchecked : we shall see in the next section that the embryo itself plays a part in maintaining the reproductive organs in a state which allows it to develop ; in the absence of an embryo this effect does not occur, and the uterine wall reverts to its inactive state.

THE SEX HORMONES

The cyclical changes so far described are anatomical changes. In laboratory animals they can be observed by dissection, and by microscopic examination of the various organs ; in human beings they have to be studied for the most part in *post mortem* material, for instance in the organs of people killed in accidents. This sort of study does not tell us how the changes are brought about : how, for instance, the uterus becomes ready for the early embryo at just the time of the liberation of an egg from the ovary.

The menstrual cycle, and other features of our reproductive physiology, are dependent on the endocrine, or ductless, glands. The most familiar sort of gland is that exemplified by sweat glands, or by the salivary glands which produce spittle : they are organs which secrete a liquid with a special function and pass it out through fine tubes, or ducts ; the tubes of the sweat glands end on the skin surface, those of the salivary glands in the mouth. There are many other such glands, for instance those which discharge digestive juices into the stomach and intestines. The endocrine glands, on the other hand, pass their secretions directly into the blood, and have no ducts to lead the secretion away.

An example of an endocrine gland is the *pituitary*, a small organ lying in a pit in the bone below the brain and above the roof of the mouth. Removal of this gland, or indeed of a particular part of it, from a male rat stops sperm production in the testes ; but extracts can be made which, injected into the animal, restore sperm production to normal. These extracts evidently contain a substance—a *hormone*—which the intact

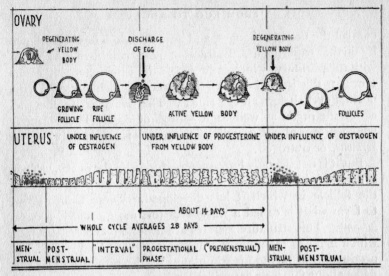

OVARY						
	DEGENERATING YELLOW BODY	DISCHARGE OF EGG		DEGENERATING YELLOW BODY		
	GROWING FOLLICLE	RIPE FOLLICLE	ACTIVE YELLOW BODY			FOLLICLES

UTERUS	UNDER INFLUENCE OF OESTROGEN	UNDER INFLUENCE OF PROGESTERONE FROM YELLOW BODY		UNDER INFLUENCE OF OESTROGEN		

ABOUT 14 DAYS

WHOLE CYCLE AVERAGES 28 DAYS

MEN-STRUAL	POST-MENSTRUAL	"INTERVAL"	PROGESTATIONAL ("PREMENSTRUAL") PHASE		MEN-STRUAL	POST-MENSTRUAL

MENSTRUAL CYCLE

A diagram showing the stages through which the ovary and uterus go during the menstrual cycle. The human "yellow body" is pink, and not yellow

gland passes into the blood and which stimulates the sperm-producing tissues of the testes. In mammals in which sexual activity is seasonal sperm ripen only in the breeding season ; this ripening is dependent on the pituitary, which produces the testis-stimulating hormone only at this time. (What stimulates the pituitary is for most species not known ; but in some it is the increase in the amount of daylight in spring).

The pituitary has many other functions besides stimulating the testes, and it produces several hormones, but here we are concerned only with the part it plays in reproduction. In a woman it has a function similar to that in a man : it stimulates the ovaries to go through their regular cycle of changes, and the whole of the menstrual cycle depends on it. The action of the pituitary on the ovaries is in the first place to stimulate egg-production ; but it has other actions, and to understand these we must go further into the way in which the ovaries work. We have seen how the cycle of egg-production in the ovaries is paralleled by a series of changes in the uterus ; if both ovaries are experimentally removed, say, from a rat, the changes in the uterus stop. Clearly the ovaries in some way

47

control the uterine changes, and how they do it has been shown by further experiment. Extracts of ovary can be made (just as with the pituitary) which induce growth of the inner wall of the uterus ; this is the same as the growth which occurs in the normal cycle before an egg ripens. The ovary is, in fact, an endocrine organ as well as a source of eggs. The hormone which brings about growth of the uterus is called the *œstrogenic hormone*, or œstrogen.

But it is not the only hormone produced by the ovary. When a ripe egg is discharged it leaves, in the ovary, the tissues of the follicle in which it has developed. These tissues grow, to form what is called a *yellow body* (or, more usually, a *corpus luteum*). This structure secretes a hormone (called *progesterone*) which helps to maintain the uterus in its prepared state. The production of this too is stimulated by the pituitary hormone. After about fourteen days, if there is no pregnancy, the yellow body collapses, and so does the inner lining of the uterus. The changes of the menstrual cycle are therefore dependent on at least three hormones, one from the pituitary and two from the ovary.

If however the egg is fertilised, and settles down in the uterus to begin development, the yellow body remains, and grows still further. And if, early in pregnancy, the yellow body is removed, abortion takes place : the uterine wall collapses and the embryo dies. (Actually, this has been observed mainly in experimental animals which have litters : in them there are several yellow bodies in each ovary, one for each egg liberated ; and all the yellow bodies have to be cut out for abortion to occur.)

The reproductive hormones are therefore the means by which the changes in the reproductive organs are synchronised. In particular, in a woman, they accurately dovetail events in the ovaries and the uterus. This is the practical significance of the menstrual cycle in women.

This is not, however, the only function of these hormones : they play an essential part also in the control of the *development* of the reproductive organs. Consider first the development of the male at the time of puberty, usually between the ages of 13 and 16 : not only does sperm production begin, but the penis enlarges ; hair appears on various parts of the body ; and growth of the larynx causes the voice to deepen. If the testes are removed before puberty these changes do not take place. This operation, castration, is commonly practised on domestic animals : male cattle become bullocks, horses geldings, and so on. It has also been extensively used in the past on human beings : eunuchs were castrated slaves who could be trusted with a man's wives ; and to provide cathedral choirs with trebles and altos promising choir boys were emasculated so that their voices should remain high. The effects of castration on general development can be prevented by the use of a hormone found in the testes : the testes, in fact, like the ovaries, are endocrine organs, secreting a hormone which plays an essential part in sexual development. Descent of the testes themselves into the scrotum, like sperm production, depends on the pituitary ; rarely a young man has testes which fail to descend, and pituitary extract can sometimes remedy the defect.

In the development of a woman the œstrogenic hormone of the ovary does work similar to that of the testis hormone in a man. The initial stimulus comes again from the pituitary, which, generally between the ages of 12 and 15, stimulates the ovaries to begin the secretion of œstrogen. This evokes a general growth of the accessory reproductive organs, the uterus, vagina and the breasts ; the menstrual cycle is set going ; and hair appears in the arm-pits and in the pubic region.

In both sexes the distinctive male and female physique, (mentioned further in chapter 9), and sexual behaviour, are partly dependent on the action of the hormones.

The reproductive hormones, then, by their many actions on different parts of the body, ensure that the organs of reproduction both *develop* and *function* in unison. Our knowledge of the way in which they work is far from complete, but the chemical nature of some of them is known, and some use has been made of them in medicine. The example of undescended testes has already been mentioned. As another we may take the common complaint of dysmenorrhea, or pain during menstruation. The origin of this pain is far from fully known, but it is sometimes at least an accompaniment of cramps or contractions of the uterine muscles—the muscles which are largely responsible for expulsion of a child when it is born. One of the actions of the hormone produced by the yellow body in the ovary is to prevent contraction of the uterus, and it is claimed that this hormone can sometimes be used to prevent the pains of menstruation ; it is however by no means an infallible source of relief, but there are other treatments which can usefully be tried.

This example has been taken because it illustrates very well the state of our knowledge of reproductive physiology. A very great deal has been learnt, mainly during the 20th century, and the new knowledge has valuable applications ; but the knowledge is exceedingly incomplete, and the application has often to be tentative and cautious.

The hormonal treatment of dysmenorrhea was based on the experimental study, often on laboratory animals, of the effects on various organs of administering the hormone in various dosages. It was, in fact, an application of knowledge carefully and laboriously acquired. It contrasts with some other treatments that at one time had a good deal of notoriety but which lacked sound physiological foundation.

The most publicised was the operation in which monkey testes (called "monkey glands", evidently to preserve the proprieties) were grafted into old men to rejuvenate them. Leaving other objections on one side, this operation is unsound because such grafts cannot survive: the grafted tissues rapidly degenerate and disappear. The operation soon became a joke, but premature attempts to make use, not of glands themselves, but of glandular extracts, have had more serious and lasting influence. G. W. Corner describes

the exploitation of endocrine preparations in the drug trade ahead of scientific knowledge. . . . Barrelfuls of extracts and millions of tablets have been fed and injected into human patients, with uncritical optimism, before the chemists and physiologists could learn the facts. The benefits of endocrine research on the reproductive glands have been almost stifled by this exploitation. Even today the practising physician finds it difficult to distinguish what is sound and practical amid the flood of well advertised endocrine drugs.

FERTILISATION

We have surveyed the organs of reproduction and the glandular mechanism by which they are co-ordinated, and we come now to the *raison d'être* of the whole complex system. We are all forty weeks older than we acknowledge, and it is the events of this neglected period that now concern us.

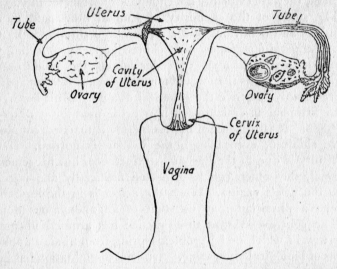

FEMALE REPRODUCTIVE ORGANS SHOWN DIAGRAMMATICALLY
One uterus, tube and ovary are shown as if cut open

The egg, on discharge from the ovary, enters the mouth of the tube which leads to the uterus. Fertilisation usually takes place in the tube : sperm, discharged into the vagina, make their way into the uterus and so into the tubes, and if an egg has recently ripened one of the sperm fertilises it. Sometimes a fertilised egg remains in the tube instead of moving down it into the uterus. After a few weeks' development internal bleeding results from rupture of the tube, and an operation becomes necessary. Fortunately this happens only in about one in three hundred pregnancies. Although only one sperm fertilises each egg, a vast number are present in each ejaculation. About a teaspoonful of semen is discharged in each coitus, perhaps 240m.[1] sperm. There is evidence that the presence of

1 Throughout the book "m." stands for "million".

many sperm is necessary to ensure fertilisation, and it is likely that they help to create the necessary chemical conditions in vagina, uterus and tubes. When infertility in a married couple is investigated it is often found that the husband's emissions consistently contain a much smaller number of active sperm than the normal ; and, although many millions of sperm are present, they are evidently not enough for normal fertility.

The study of the chemistry of seminal fluid, and of the numbers and behaviour of sperm, has been stimulated by the use of *artificial insemination* in stockbreeding. By collecting the semen of a selected male a breeder can use the male to serve many more females than would normally be possible, and so can more rapidly improve the genetical qualities of his herd. In man artificial insemination is now being used for a different purpose. It is sometimes impossible for a married couple to have children, even though the woman is normal. If the difficulty is due to the husband's impotence, but his semen is normal, the semen can be collected artificially and injected into the wife's vagina. When the defect is in the husband's semen a physician may use that of an anonymous donor.

The controversy that this practice has aroused illustrates the way in which social problems spring from human applications of biological knowledge. Artificial insemination has been attacked on religious and moral grounds, and complaints have been made that it raises grave legal difficulties. It has been said that the use of a donor's semen is adultery, and it is further condemned because the production of donor semen involves masturbation ; (an interesting light is thrown on this view by the facts that in all human communities investigated masturbation has proved to be exceedingly common, if not universal ; and that it is known also in a number of other mammalian species, e.g. some monkeys, dogs and rabbits) ; and it has been complained that a child produced by artificial insemination is legally "illegitimate", and this leads to various difficulties, especially over the inheritance of property.

The supporters of artificial insemination hold that it should be regarded as yet another example of technical advances giving us further control over nature ; that if it is applied with the consent of both man and wife it can give, and has given, the greatest satisfaction to both ; and that although it does raise moral and legal problems, they can be solved. It has further been claimed that the religious objections are in much the same terms as those in which the churches opposed the use of anæsthesia in childbirth a century ago.

The history of other advances in human biology and medicine suggests that artificial insemination will continue to cause controversy, but that it will nevertheless be used, and its use will increase.

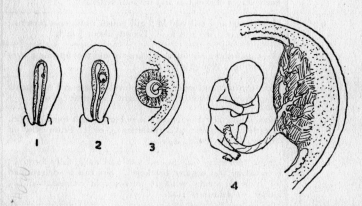

IMPLANTATION AND DEVELOPMENT OF THE HUMAN EMBRYO

1. The fertilised egg is implanted in the wall of the uterus ; 2. It becomes surrounded by uterine tissues ; 3. A placenta develops, composed of tissues derived from the egg intimately mixed with the tissues of the uterus ; 4. The foetus and placenta enlarge, and the placenta comes to be localised on one side and connected with the foetus by the umbilical cord

OURSELVES UNBORN

The timetable of pregnancy, and of the growth of the child, is conveniently reckoned not from fertilisation, but from the beginning of the last menstrual period. On this scheme the most probable time of fertilisation is the end of the second week. The fertilised egg then spends about a week travelling down the tube and floating in the uterus. During this time development begins : the egg-cell divides, and successive cell-divisions give rise to a ball of cells. (Cells have already been mentioned in

TABLE 1 : TIMETABLE OF DEVELOPMENT

WEEK *after last menstruation*	DEVELOPMENT
2 (end)	Fertilisation
3	Egg travels down tube into uterus ; begins to divide
4	Implantation in wall of uterus
5	Early stages of skeleton and nervous system
6	Head, heart and tail visible ; gill pouch rudiments present ; rudiments of arms and legs. Length about $\frac{1}{4}$ inch
7	Chest and abdomen formed ; fingers and toes appear ; eyes developing. About $\frac{1}{2}$ inch
8	Face, features and external ears developing ; gill rudiments disappearing. About $\frac{7}{8}$ inch, weight 1 gramme ($\frac{1}{28}$ oz.)
9	Face completely developed ; now resembles a human child. Length 1.2 inch, weight 2 grammes ($\frac{1}{14}$ oz.). From now on embryo usually called a *fœtus*
14	Limbs, including fingers and toes and nails, fully formed ; external genital organs developed. Sex can be determined by trained person without microscopic examination. 3 inches, 30 grammes (1 oz.)
18	Movements (quickening) begin ; heart can be heard ; hair all over body ; eyebrows and eyelashes. 8½ inches, 180 grammes (6½ oz.)
23	Head hair appears. 12 inches, 450 grammes (16 oz.)
27	Eyes open. 14 inches, 875 grammes (31 oz.)
32	16 inches, 1,425 grammes (3 lb. 2 oz.). If born now can survive, given special care
36	18 inches, 2,375 grammes (5 lb. 4 oz.). Better chance of survival now, in eighth month, than in seventh (contrary to commonly held belief)
40	Full term. Skin covered with cheese-like material. Head hair typically 1 inch long ; may be other hair on shoulders, but soon disappears. Head still very large relative to body. 20 inches, 3,250 grammes (7 lb. 4 oz.) *All measurements are averages, and there are many wide departures from them, especially in the later months*

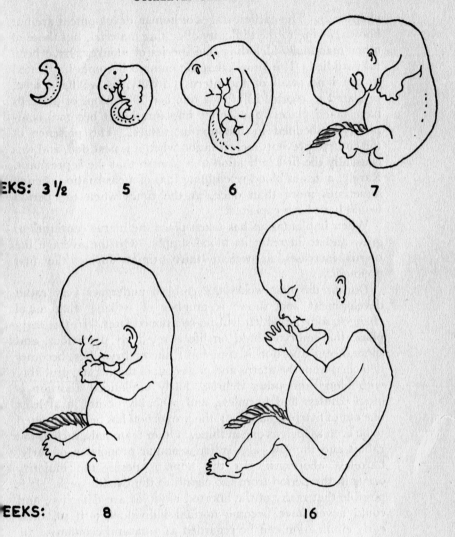

HUMAN EMBRYOS
The umbilical cord is shown in the three largest

chapter 2). The earliest stages of human development are not known, owing to the difficulty of getting material, but those of other mammals, including one species of monkey, have been fully studied. It is known that the embryo becomes implanted in the inner wall of the uterus (already, as we have seen, prepared to receive it) after a number of divisions of the cells have taken place. Soon after implantation it becomes completely embedded in the uterine tissues. The presence of the embryo prevents menstruation when it is next due, and this is usually the first indication to a woman that she is pregnant. Rarely, a loss of blood resembling that of menstruation occurs, sometimes more than once, at the times when the period would have been expected.

When implantation has taken place the uterus continues to grow and to increase its blood supply. On the average the uterus increases in weight thirty times during the first pregnancy.

During the first weeks the embryo undergoes very rapid development and shows a number of striking anatomical changes, some of which will be mentioned later. In this early phase the embryo's hold on life is relatively precarious, and spontaneous abortion is common : the embryo dies, becomes detached from the uterus and passes out of the vagina, probably with blood and other debris. Early unplanned abortion is often painless and harmless, and probably occurs in at least one out of five pregnancies ; the proportion has been estimated to be even as high as one in three. Other mammals, such as the rabbit and the sow, also suffer a similar proportion of early, harmless abortions. In the human species the majority occur in the period from the eighth to the twelfth week. It is possible that many of the aborted embryos are defective, and could never have become normal individuals ; if so, their early elimination can be regarded as a natural economy.

RECAPITULATION OF ANCESTRAL CHARACTERS

A feature of early development, much discussed but not often well understood, is the so-called recapitulation of ancestral stages. It is sometimes said that we go through a fish stage representing the fish stage of our evolution, and it is even said that we "climb our family tree" during our embryonic existence. Neither of these statements is true. What actually happens does indeed reflect our evolutionary history, but the details are complex.

The evolution of the human species is discussed more fully in the next chapter ; here we need say only that about 300m. years ago our ancestors were certainly some kind of primitive fish, and that on land the stages in our ancestry included a cold-blooded reptilian phase and, later, warm-blooded primitive mammals with hair instead of scales and young which were born alive instead of hatched from eggs.

What traces of this evolutionary history can we find in individual development ? The most obvious are found about four weeks after fertilisation (week 6 in the table). Externally the embryo seems to have rudimentary gills (though actually they never fully develop) ; it has a long tail relative to the whole body ; and in general it resembles, not a fish, but a *fish embryo*. Internally the resemblance is carried further : for instance, the arrangement of the blood vessels is fish-like, and the principal muscles of the body are divided into segments which in a fish become those we can easily see when we eat, say, cod or salmon. All these structures undergo a rapid and complex transformation, and within a few weeks there is little obvious trace of them. This transformation is, on the whole, directly into the structural arrangement typical of the human being : it is not possible to discern, for instance, a phase in embryonic development corresponding to the reptilian stage in evolution, although certain parts of the body do show temporary arrangements which resemble those in a reptile. Actually, it is possible to find traces of our pre-human ancestry at every stage in development, including the adult : there are, for instance, the much commented-on muscles which a few gifted people can use to waggle their ears, but which in most of us are ineffective ; most mammals can move their ears in the direction of particular sounds, and in us these muscles are a vestige reminding us of a mobile-eared ancestry.

We can see, then, traces of our evolutionary history in our development, but the study of embryology by no means saves us the trouble of trying to work out how we evolved by other methods, such as those described in the next chapter. There are other examples of the ways in which development fails to reflect evolution. Take, for example, the shape of the face. In most mammals there is a prominent snout, but in man the face is flat. If there were a straightforward recapitulation of ancestral characters we should expect that the human embryo would develop a snout and then lose it. In fact, no snout ever appears in human development. In mammals which have snouts the forward growth of the face occurs relatively late ; all early mammalian embryos are flat-faced. Thus the shape of the face in man is an embryonic characteristic retained in the adult. This is the opposite of what would be expected if the simple idea of recapitulation were true.

To sum up, we can find indications of our ancestry at every stage of our development, including the adult, but there is no simple recapitulation. After all, it is not only the adult structure that undergoes evolutionary change : the whole of our life-history has been subject to change ; at some stages, however, the difference from the ancestral arrangement is rather less than at others.

Pregnancy and the Placenta

The most obvious of the evolutionary changes undergone by mammalian embryos are those connected with development in the mother's uterus, instead of from an egg laid outside the body. The egg of a reptile, like that of a bird, has a large yolk which provides the food on which the embryo lives until it hatches. In a mammal there is no yolk at all : all food is supplied by the mother, and the structure of the embryo is adapted to this parasitic mode of life. At implantation the egg, as we have seen, is already divided into a number of cells. Not all these cells are destined to form the child : some of them form what are called *extra-embryonic* tissues—a term which means simply that they are outside the embryo. The embryo is completely surrounded by these tissues and, once implantation is complete, the tissues in turn are surrounded by those of the uterine wall.

The extra-embryonic tissues thrust minute, finger-like processes into the uterine tissues, and so greatly increase the area over which food material can diffuse into the embryo. This is the beginning of the formation of the *placenta*, the organ of interchange between mother and child. It is constituted partly by embryonic and partly by maternal tissues, and is eventually shed as the *after-birth* soon after the child is born. The placenta grows rapidly in the early stages, and is still, at full term, about the same weight as the child. After the first few weeks it becomes localised on one side of the embryo, and connected to the embryo only by the umbilical cord. The cord contains blood vessels which carry blood in both directions between the placenta and the child, and it has to be cut when the child is born. The navel is the scar marking the junction of the cord with the belly.

ENLARGEMENT OF THE UTERUS IN PREGNANCY
The virgin uterus (V), compared with the uterus at full term

The blood and blood vessels in the umbilical cord are all part of the embryonic system : the mother's blood does not mingle with that of the child, though in the placenta they are separated only by exceedingly fine membranes. Across these membranes pass the substances exchanged : oxygen and food from mother to child, carbon dioxide and other waste products in the opposite direction.

The demands of the embryo for certain foodstuffs put a strain on the mother which may injure her if she is inadequately fed or otherwise in poor health. It is not the general demand for food that is important : it is a fallacy that a pregnant woman needs a great deal of extra food. The average net gain in weight during a first pregnancy is about 23 lb., and during later pregnancies about 21 lb. The child and the placenta each account for about one-third of the gain, the rest being due to the enlarged uterus, increase in body fat, and the "bag of waters" which surrounds the embryo and protects it from injury. The whole of the gain in weight takes place after the 16th week ; before then there is no gain, and there may be a loss. But a gain of 23 lb. in 34 weeks is not very much, and the extra daily intake of food required is quite small.

In western countries, where there is little gross under-nutrition or malnutrition, the nutritional difficulties of pregnancy are due to special shortages. The old maxim "a tooth for every child" is based on the fact that calcium deficiency is common in mothers. A pregnant woman who gets too little calcium in her food transfers calcium from her bones and teeth to the embryo ; as a result, her skeleton and teeth may be weakened ; the effect on the child is thus reduced. Similarly, according to one investigation, anæmia due to iron shortage occurs in at least one American woman in three in the last three months of pregnancy, owing to the demands of the embryo for iron. Deficiency of calcium, iron and other dietary essentials, notably vitamins, can be avoided by giving pregnant women a good diet, as we shall see in chapter 12.

Some other problems of pregnancy are not so easily solved. Strangely, predicting its duration is one. The birth of a child is predicted on the assumption that it will take place 280 days, or 40 weeks, after the first day of the last menstruation. 280 days is indeed approximately the mean duration of pregnancy, found from studies of large numbers of normal births ; but, as most parents know, there are many wide departures from it. In one study of 537 white American women, all of whom bore living children, the results were as follows :

	per cent
before 266th day	12.7
2nd week before (days 266-272)	12.3
1st week before (days 273-279)	22.0
on 280th day	3.7
1st week after (days 281-287)	24.2
2nd week after (days 288-294)	15.6
after 294th day	9.4

If the percentage for each day is taken it is found to be highest for the 280th day, and to fall away slowly both before and after ; thus 280 days is the mode as well as the mean length of pregnancy ; but it will be seen how impossible it is to predict accurately in any particular case.

It is comparatively easy to make statistical studies such as the above, given secretarial help and a punch card system ; but other problems of pregnancy require more elaborate study. The most obvious are the so-called *toxæmias* of pregnancy—an expression based on the belief that they are due to "poisons in the blood". The toxæmia of early pregnancy is pernicious vomiting, an exaggeration of the common morning sickness. Some nausea or vomiting is exceedingly common early in pregnancy : according to Guttmacher it is severe in about one-third of all cases and mild in a third ; the rest are entirely free. "Many an ink-well has been drained dry over the cause of vomiting in pregnancy, but we are only slightly wiser than when the first quill scratched about it." In the mild cases it disappears about the twelfth week, but the most severe cases, which are rare, require special treatment. The toxæmias of late pregnancy are all accompanied by high blood pressure, and usually by a disturbance of the chemistry of the body which causes an excessive retention of water. In an extreme case, now very rare when there is good ante-natal care, convulsions develop.

It is general ante-natal care, especially proper feeding, that is most effective in countering these dangers, and where it is practised it has already greatly reduced the incidence of serious

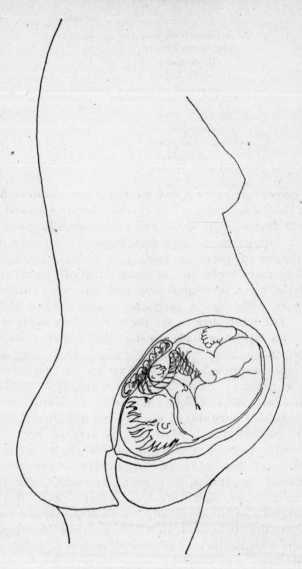

FULL-TERM HUMAN FŒTUS

cases. But the causes of the toxæmias of pregnancy are still unknown, and since about one pregnancy in fifteen, in an advanced country such as the United States, is complicated by one of them, they would repay extensive research. Already there are indications that study of disturbances of the endocrine system in pregnancy can be of value.

Much the same applies to childbirth itself, the aspect of pregnancy which probably looms largest in most minds. The pangs of childbirth seem to have been taken for granted throughout history, and when, a century ago, anæsthesia was invented, its use in childbirth was condemned as "unnatural" and "immoral". Actually, the most obvious objection to anæsthesia (which causes unconsciousness) is that it is not safe ; it also deprives the mother of the unique pleasure felt on holding her new-born child. Today the emphasis is rather on analgesia, which is the relief of pain without loss of consciousness. Quite recently new and better analgesics have been found, and they are coming to be widely applied. It is however claimed that pain can be largely prevented without the use of drugs, by instruction of the mother in the nature of pregnancy and in what is required of her during the actual birth. Fear of pregnancy, largely due to ignorance, is common, and is considered to contribute a great deal to the discomforts of childbirth.

More research, and wider application of what is known by means of improved health services, are needed along all these lines : improvement of ante-natal care, analgesia and psychological preparation of the mother. Meanwhile important facts have been brought out by an entirely different approach. In a primitive community nearly all women begin to bear children soon after puberty : the average age of the mother at the first birth is perhaps seventeen. In advanced communities, especially today, the age is much greater. Statistical studies of maternal and infant mortality have shown that both tend to rise in proportion to the age of the mother ; probably the best age for having a first child is 22. Further enquiry has suggested that subsequent children should be born at intervals of about 24 months.

It is important to be clear on exactly what this signifies.

It is not that a married couple should despair of bringing up a family if the woman has, say, reached her thirties without having a child. Ante-natal and obstetric care has advanced so far today that, even when the mother is over forty, the successful birth of a first child is no longer a matter for astonishment. Certainly, if early child-bearing is practicable, it should be encouraged, but the significance of the figures quoted in the previous paragraph is for society as a whole, rather than for the individual. The reasons for late marriage and delayed maternity are mostly economic. If social organisation obliges women to delay child-bearing to the detriment of their health and that of their children, the obvious conclusion is that the social organisation should be changed. These points will be further discussed in chapter 14.

"This Fair Defect of Nature"

The study of human reproduction and of early development is obviously worth while for the knowledge it gives us on how to improve the lot of parents and children. This has been a main theme of the present chapter. To end it we may turn to the much more general question asked, with some humour, by Milton in the passage quoted at the chapter head. Even if we do not agree that the division of humanity into two sexes is a defect in nature, or that of the two sexes the "feminine" can be more easily dispensed with, we may still be curious to know what is the biological significance of sexual reproduction and development from an egg. The question has been clearly asked and answered by Abercrombie : "we must," he writes,

ask (sometimes a little peevishly) why development is so drastic a remodelling. What is gained by starting from a single cell ? Admitting the necessity for reproduction, why should not an animal simply release an already highly organised fragment of itself ? Such an offspring could then develop into a new adult without the necessity of building from the very foundations. Reproduction in this *vegetative* way does indeed occur in some groups of animals, and more prominently in plants. But from its relative infrequency we may infer that it is at a disadvantage compared with the sexual method . . .

To assess the value of sexual reproduction we have to recall that all living things undergo evolution. From this point of view we see that

> The advantage of the sexual method lies in the fact that the act of fertilisation brings together heritable material (the genes) from two individuals, the two parents, and combines it in one offspring. The result is that favourable genes which have originated (by mutation) in separate individuals can become associated in one individual. And new combinations of genes whose value lies in their interaction . . . can similarly be realised. . . . In vegetative reproduction combination of genes in this way is impossible. . . . Sexual reproduction thus confers a gain in the flexibility and efficiency of evolutionary advance which has apparently greatly outweighed the disadvantages of its complexity. . . .

Fertilisation between two large bodies, composed of many cells, would be an exceedingly complex procedure, and nothing of the sort has ever been evolved. Consequently, to get the advantages of sexual reproduction even the largest animals retain a stage in their life history of microscopic size, namely, the fertilised egg ; and fertilisation "has become not only a method of recombining genes, but a stimulus which sets off an elaborate developmental mechanism."

We end this chapter, therefore, by emphasising that man is a product of evolution ; in the next the evidence for this statement is more fully set forth, and the course of human evolution is described.

Part Two

HUMAN DIVERSITY

MAN is a product of evolution. The main features which distinguish him from his nearest living relatives, the apes, are his large brain, manual dexterity and the power of speech: these, with other special characters, make possible man's unique form of social organisation.

Only one human species exists today, and the physical differences, such as skin colour, by which human types are classified are of only trivial significance, although for social or political reasons they are sometimes given a spurious importance. All human groups or "races" include individuals of a wide range of ability and social worth ; there is no justification for saying that one group is innately inferior to another, and the social achievements of each group depend largely on the natural resources and amenities available. Theories of the inferiority or criminality of particular groups often arise from the political needs of a dominant group, such as foreign conquerors or employers of cheap labour. Much ability is wasted, and injustice caused, by the inferior position which the colonial and other backward peoples occupy. Similar waste and injustice occur within each country in which there are large unprivileged classes of poor people. In most countries women form an unprivileged class.

CHAPTER 5

FROM APE TO MAN

GENETICS, our main topic so far, is a study of differences between individuals. We come now, in this and the next four chapters, to differences between large groups. Today few dispute that men, like other animals and plants and indeed the earth, the sun and the stars, are a product of evolution. The present chapter deals with the stages of the evolution of men from primitive apes, and the variety of human types that have existed in the last million years.

THE EVIDENCE OF ROCKS AND FOSSILS

The main evidence that the animals and plants of today have evolved from very different previous forms is based on our knowledge of the changes that have occurred in the earth's crust. For at least the past 500 million years ice, wind and rain have been eroding the surface of the earth, while in other parts rivers and sea have been depositing layers of new rock made up largely of the eroded particles. If we dig deep into the earth we find that the rocks are arranged in layers, and where there has been no violent disturbance such as those due to volcanoes or earthquakes the older rocks are the deeper. (Actually, sorting out the different types of rock, and determining their origin, which is a part of the science of geology, is a very tricky business ; but it has been successfully done in many parts of the world).

Each type of rock that has been laid down by sea or river water contains its own characteristic fossils ; so does the coal-bearing rock that was deposited in primeval forests. Fossils are the remains of plants and animals : as a rule only the hard parts, such as bones, are preserved, and they undergo a chemical change in which the organic material is replaced by rock substance, without alteration of the original structure. The skeletons of giant "dinosaurs" that one sees in the museums are made, not of bone, but of rock in the form of the original bony skeleton.

Not only can the order in time of the different rocks be determined ; their ages also can be roughly calculated in various ways. The calculations show that the evolution both of the rocks and of living things has taken some hundreds of millions of years. The group of back-boned animals (the vertebrates), to which we belong, began in the sea more than 300m. years ago, and at first the only vertebrates were fish-like animals. If the fossils of successive layers are studied it is found that some early fishes gradually developed the capacity to live on land, and so gave rise to the land vertebrates. The earliest land vertebrates were amphibia (a group now represented by frogs and newts), but for the greater part of the time after this the most prominent land vertebrates were reptiles, including the notorious dinosaurs, pterodactyls and so forth. One branch of these reptiles developed feathers, wings and warm-bloodedness, and became birds.

Meanwhile, even before the great reptiles evolved, an entirely different branch of the reptiles specialised in a different way. The original peg-like teeth (as in a crocodile today) became more complex, as ours are : some became grinders, others came to be similar to front and eye-teeth. During the period of the great reptiles some of these forms with complex teeth developed warm blood and the capacity to bear young alive (instead of laying eggs) ; we do not yet know when, because the skeletons that remain do not tell us. At all events it is certain that by the time the great reptiles perished, evidently as a result of drastic climatic changes involving the whole world, there were mammals in existence ready to take their place.

The mammals, the class of warm-blooded, furry vertebrates that includes our own species, have been the main land vertebrates for 60m. years. We have an enormous mass of fossil remains of some groups : we can trace every detail of the evolution of some modern hoofed mammals, and of large carnivores such as lions and tigers, from small, undistinguished creatures rather like shrew-mice. Other groups of mammals have left fewer fossil remains, because they did not live in surroundings which favoured fossilisation. Among these less well-recorded orders is unfortunately that of the primates, the one

6

that includes the monkeys, apes and men—nearly all forest-dwellers. Moreover, the fossil record becomes exceptionally thin when we come to the precursors of man himself. This is probably because the immediate ancestors of man were not only forest-dwellers but comparatively rare animals. Nevertheless it is already possible to give a clear, if not very detailed, account of the evolution of men from ape-like creatures.

The Causes of Evolution

Before we come to this account we must see something of how evolutionary change has come about. The man whose researches finally brought scientists to accept the theory of organic evolution was Charles Darwin. Among a number of evolutionists of the 18th and 19th centuries Darwin not only presented a mass of evidence for the fact of evolution : he also produced the first convincing theory of how it had occurred. At the same time as Alfred Russell Wallace he put forward the theory of *natural selection* (often miscalled the "survival of the fittest"). The theory will be stated here in the modern form, which differs only in detail from that of Darwin and Wallace.

Natural selection depends on two things : first, inherited variation ; second, a selective mortality, so that some types tend to live longer than others. *Inherited variation* has already been discussed at length, in chapters 2 and 3. Its agents are the genes, and mutation ensures a continuous supply of new forms. For *selective mortality* we have to assume the production of offspring in excess, in each generation. In a population of constant size this excess will not survive, and with the excess will disappear certain inherited characteristics. This last assumption is perfectly justified. In every plant or animal species studied, even the least fertile such as elephants, gannets and man, many more offspring are produced than are needed to maintain populations at a constant level. There is always a high mortality in the young and a considerable death-rate among adults. This mortality is undoubtedly one of the means by which natural selection occurs.

This account of the machinery of evolution is not just guesswork. In some instances evolutionary change has been observed while it was taking place. For example, in some species of moths black varieties have replaced paler forms in industrial areas where everything is covered with soot : the black types are less conspicuous, and so better equipped to evade their enemies. This is an example of the replacement of one *variety* by another. Darwin thought that varieties were incipient species, and today we have good evidence that he was right.

One of the most useful ways of deciding whether to call two closely related types separate species is to find out whether they can be crossed and made to yield fertile offspring. The horse and the ass, which are different species, can be crossed, but the mule which results is sterile. In some instances crosses of this sort, between fairly widely different types, give offspring with impaired fertility. The gypsy moth, of which the Latin name is *Lymantria dispar* (indicating that only one species is involved) is found in a number of different areas, including Western Europe and Japan. Each area has its own particular "race", and these races can be crossed ; but the resulting offspring usually breed among themselves only with difficulty, if at all. Evidently the different geographical varieties of *Lymantria* are on the way to becoming distinct species, and this is another instance of evolutionary change which can be observed in progress.

It is clear that to observe evolutionary change directly, save in a fragmentary way, is impossible, because of the time-scale of the changes. Nevertheless, the evidence of the succession of rocks, with their wealth of fossil remains, together with studies of the contemporary variety of plant and animal life, give us a remarkably complete outline both of the course and the causes of evolution.

PREHUMAN FOSSILS

The preliminaries to the evolution of man took place between 30 and 60m. years ago, when the tailless apes appeared as a group separate from that of the ordinary monkeys. The monkeys leap from one tree-hold to another, using all four limbs for grasping ; the apes on the other hand make first-rate trapeze artists, since their normal way of moving in trees is by swinging with their hands.

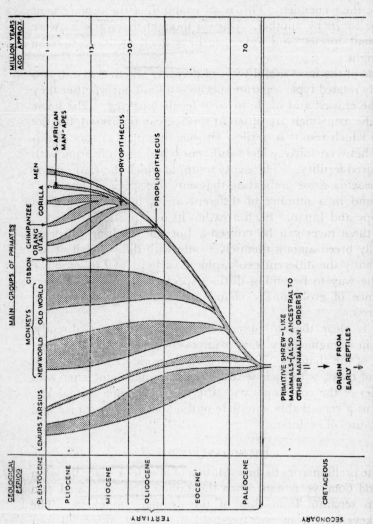

FAMILY TREE OF THE PRIMATES—LEMURS, MONKEYS, APES AND MEN. This diagram illustrates only the main relationships of the primate groups. It is not known exactly when the various branches diverged, nor even for certain the exact date of the South-African man-apes.

But we have no intimate knowledge of the life of the early apes : we have as yet direct knowledge only of their teeth and lower jaws ; only these, the least destructible parts, have survived in sufficient numbers to be found. One lower jaw, from Fayum, near the Nile, is called *Propliopithecus*. It belonged to an ape far smaller than any we know today, perhaps not more than eighteen inches high. It lived at a time when the main lines of mammalian evolution had already appeared ; in particular, the primates (the order of lemurs, monkeys and apes) were already represented by the main groups into which we divide them today, with the monkeys of the New World and the Old World already distinct.

The figure opposite shows the geological periods into which the Tertiary period, the period of mammals, is divided. Propliopithecus belongs to the Oligocene, a time when apes or their ancestors were evidently rare. But in the next period, the Miocene, some millions of years later, we find that apes are comparatively widespread and common. Today, apes (apart from man himself) are found only in south-east Asia and Central Africa, whereas the Miocene fossils have been found also in North and East Africa, and widely dispersed in Europe and Asia.

Some of the most important of the known Miocene apes are assigned to the genus *Dryopithecus*. These fossils are themselves found in Central Asia, Europe and Africa, and closely similar ones have been discovered in India. The grinding teeth show resemblances in pattern both to those of the chimpanzee and gorilla, and to our own, and it is believed that *Dryopithecus* is near the line of ancestry of all three species, and possibly of that of the orang-utan as well. What we need is a complete skeleton. An arm and a leg bone have been found, possibly belonging to this genus ; they suggest that *Dryopithecus* had shorter arms and longer legs, relative to the body, than have present-day apes : in other words, *Dryopithecus* may have had proportions half-way between those of apes and men. While this book was being written other Miocene fossils of great interest were being discovered in Kenya. The jaws and teeth of some fossil apes had already been found there, in 1931, and assigned to three new genera of which *Proconsul* is the most important. The skull of *Proconsul* has now been found ; it is light compared with those of modern apes, and it lacks their heavy brow ridges and very projecting muzzle ; in these respects it has more in common with the monkeys than with the apes. Bones of the leg and foot suggest that *Proconsul* did not move in trees as modern apes do, but that they were more ground-living in habit. According to Le Gros Clark, the director of the expedition which discovered them, they "indicate that these early Miocene apes were lightly built and active creatures, capable of running and leaping with considerable agility."

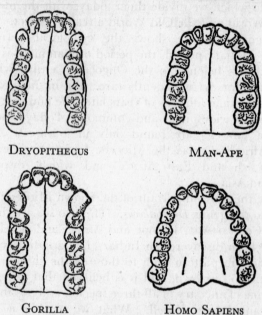

DRYOPITHECUS   MAN-APE

GORILLA   HOMO SAPIENS

UPPER JAWS AND TEETH

Dryopithecus has a dental arch like that of a modern ape, i.e. "square" ; *Plesianthropus*, one of the South African man-apes, has the curved, human type. Note the massive canine in the gorilla, not found in the others

As links between men and apes another group of recently discovered African fossils are even more important. They are called collectively the Australopithecinæ, but here we shall refer to them as the South African man-apes. (They have also

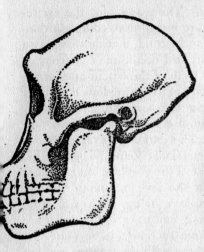

MAN-APE

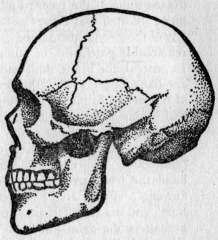

HOMO SAPIENS

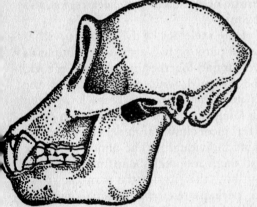

CHIMPANZEE

SKULLS OF APES AND MAN

The South African man-ape has a cranium of similar size to that of the modern chimpanzee, but in other features is more human : note especially the teeth, and the absence of heavy ridges on the cranium

been referred to as "Dartians", after Professor Dart who first discovered them. They have nothing to do with Australia : "australo-" means "southern").

As the first draft of this chapter is being written, in May, 1947, letters are appearing in the scientific weekly, *Nature*, announcing further discoveries of fossil man-apes, and it is only a few weeks since a congress of scientists was held in Kenya to discuss some of the recent finds. The reasons for the excitement are first, that these fossils are much more complete than any of those so far mentioned ; and second, that they display a remarkable patchwork of human and non-human characters. In general, the brain, skull and teeth of these man-apes are of ape-like proportions, but the details of structure show a number of similarities to man. Like the gorilla and chimpanzee, they had brains of about half the size of our own, and heavy protruding jaws with large teeth. The estimated average endocranial capacity of the first ten skulls found is 500 cubic centimetres—rather less than that of the gorilla. On the other hand the teeth are arranged in the jaw in human fashion, forming a curved arch ; the canines (or eye-teeth) are quite small, and not tusk-like as in apes ; and the grinding teeth are human in the details of their construction : these man-apes chewed their food as we do, and not with the rotating motion of the apes. In the skull the brows lack the heavy ridges above the eyes characteristic of apes, and the cheek region also was human in construction.

We have knowledge of the skeletons of the limbs as well as the skull. In one instance parts of two arm bones (humerus and ulna) and a skull were found together in one lump of rock, and could therefore be assigned with certainty all to the same animal. (This is important, because there have been instances of bones being found moderately close to each other and giving rise to fierce but inconclusive arguments on whether they belonged to the same individual.) The almost complete pelvic skeleton, and wrist, thigh and ankle-bone fragments have also been found. They show that in size the man-apes were smaller than most men, perhaps resembling human pigmies. But, more important, the limb bones are found to be in structure (though not in size) typically human, even in detail. There is thus no doubt that the limbs of the South African man-apes resembled ours, and that these creatures walked erect as we do. The thumbs too resemble ours, and not those of modern apes, in being efficient grasping organs, probably capable of manipulating tools and weapons. The ankle bones, however, were partly ape-like, giving a greater mobility. The erect posture is confirmed also by the structure of the base of the skull, where it joins the vertebral column : the skull was held erect, like ours, not poked forward like that of an ape. The ape-men lived on the ground, on grasslands, instead of being forest-dwellers.

The picture that emerges, then, is one of a small, man-like body, with a head more ape-like than human but having some human features. It is therefore natural to ask whether the ape-men had developed greater intelligence than true apes. In size of brain they were no different, and so it is, perhaps, unlikely for that reason alone. But it has been suggested that the man-apes used tools. Baboon skulls have been found near some of the remains, fractured as if they had been struck by a blunt instrument. Professor Dart has consequently suggested that the man-apes were at least intelligent enough to hunt and to kill their prey with weapons. Perhaps, before this book is in print, more evidence will be available on this point. If Dart's view is confirmed it may be necessary to abandon the expression "man-ape", and to refer to the South African fossils as men.

Fossil Man

The last sentence provokes the question, where is the line drawn between man and not-man ? Clearly, if we had a complete series of fossils, as we have for some other mammals, we should have to choose a quite arbitrary point in the series to mark the division. As it is, there are two possible sorts of criteria for distinguishing human from pre-human types. First, we can use anatomical features : this, indeed, is the obvious thing to do, since fossils give us direct information on structure, but only indirect knowledge of anything else. So a palæontologist, William Howells, says that "man zoologically became man when he first walked erect on the ground, or at least developed an arch to his foot." Second, we can say that the use of specially manufactured tools is diagnostic of man.

It is, of course, purely a matter of terminology—of nomenclature—whether we call the South African man-apes "men" (or, more technically, Hominidæ). What is important is our knowledge that creatures existed with this curious combination of human-type limbs and ape-like skull. The fossils we possess

GEOLOGICAL PERIOD	ICE AGES	HUMAN TYPES	CULTURES	THOUSANDS OF YEARS AGO
RECENT			Mesolithic, Neolithic AND LATER	TO - DAY
P L E I S T O C E N E	FOURTH ICE-AGE	HOMO SAPIENS	Upper Palaeolithic [GREAT VARIETY OF IMPLEMENTS OF STONE, BONE, IVORY & HORN; CAVE DRAWINGS]	100
		Piltdown skull		
	THIRD INTER-GLACIAL	NEANDERTHAL MEN	Mousterian [WIDER VARIETY OF STONE TOOLS, OFTEN MADE BY FLAKING, WITH VERY SHARP EDGES; BURIAL OF DEAD WITH THEIR TOOLS]	
	THIRD ICE-AGE			200
				300
	SECOND INTER-GLACIAL	Swanscombe skull	Acheulian [IMPROVED HAND AXES WITH SHARPER EDGES]	
		JAVA and PEKIN MEN		400
	SECOND ICE-AGE			
	FIRST INTER-GLACIAL		Abbevillian [LARGE BUT CRUDE STONE HAND AXES]	500
	FIRST ICE-AGE			600

THE PLEISTOCENE AND RECENT PERIODS, AND FOSSIL MEN

The chart shows the approximate dates and relative positions in time of the main types of men and their tools and weapons. Authorities are not unanimous on the time-scale of the period, and the one shown here is based on that of Professor F. E. Zeuner. The position of the Piltdown skull is based on very recent research (see page 87) probably come from the Pliocene, and so are earlier than the earliest known men. It seems likely that man-apes of very similar structure were also ancestors of men.

By the middle Pleistocene, perhaps half-a-million years ago, several varieties or species of men existed in Java and China, and may have existed elsewhere. The first discovered, and among the most ancient, was the famous ape-man of Java, called *Pithecanthropus erectus* by his discoverer. This name was at first given to nothing more than a skull cap, a thigh bone and a few teeth. From these remains the discoverer, Dubois, inferred the existence of an exceedingly primitive man, with a brain midway in size between a man's and a gorilla's, and teeth intermediate in structure, but with erect posture. This diagnosis has been confirmed, not only by further discoveries in Java, but also by much more extensive discoveries near Pekin. Pekin man has been called *Sinanthropus pekinensis*, but is now regarded by many as a variety of *Pithecanthropus*, or at most a closely similar species. Moreover, some authorities prefer to call both Java and Pekin man *Homo erectus*, to indicate a close kinship with ourselves.

Today, in 1949, fragments from about forty Pekin men and women have been found ; none is anything like complete, but we can be certain, not only of the similarity to the Java men, but also that the brain size on the average was greater : the males had an average brain capacity of about 1,100 cubic centimetres, which is 200 above Java man and about 250 below us. They varied, however, from 900 to 1,250. Limb bones are fully human in structure in both the Java and the Pekin men. As for height, Java man seems to have resembled us (about five feet six inches), while Pekin man had a height of about five feet.

The evidence for the use of tools by Java man is not complete: stone implements have been found in the same deposits as the skeletal remains, but that is not absolutely conclusive. On the other hand it is certain that Pekin man used stone implements, and their structure shows that he was right-handed like us. They include heavy choppers, and smaller flaked scraping tools. They belong to the old stone age, but are not the most primitive of all known stone implements. The main food was

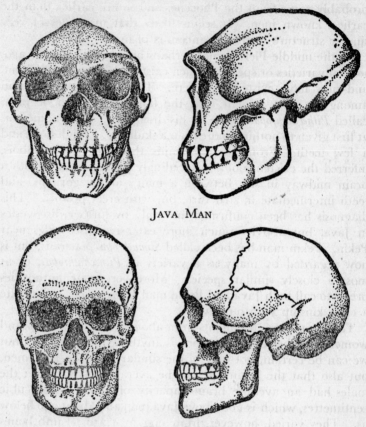

JAVA MAN

HOMO SAPIENS

evidently venison, to judge by the bones found in the caves, but many other species were hunted. There is evidence from the condition of the bones that Pekin man also killed and ate other members of his own species : in other words, that Pekin man was a cannibal. Moreover, he may have cooked his food. Certainly, there are patches of blackened earth which show that he had fire. From all this we can suspect that he also had speech, since it is probable that the construction of tools and the use of language developed together.

Other types of men were in existence at about the time when the Java and Pekin men lived. One of the features of early

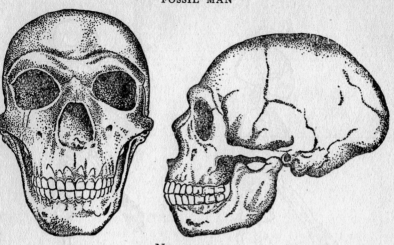

NEANDERTHAL

HUMAN SKULLS

Java man (*Pithecanthropus*) has the smallest cranial capacity of the three types, and the heaviest bony ridges. Modern man has the most lightly constructed skull, no snout, and correspondingly well-developed nose and chin (see figure on page 88)

man is the thicker and heavier bone of the skull, compared with our own. This applies to the Java and Pekin skulls, but even more to some more recently discovered fragments. The average thickness of the bones of the brain case of Java man is about twice that of modern man, but the new specimens, though fragmentary, show an even more massive structure. The most important discoveries of these heavyweights were made, once again, in Java, and one authority believes that the complete individual must have been "much bigger than any living gorilla". If this is true, there were certainly giants in the earth in those days, and it is possible that some of them were among our ancestors.

Anatomically, apart from bone thickness, these men belong to the same group as the men of Java and Pekin. They may have been no more than a variety, or "race", of *Homo erectus*. The search for more specimens was interrupted by war ; when it is resumed it will perhaps be possible to come to a more definite conclusion on their significance in human evolution.

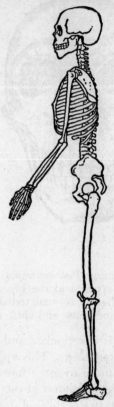

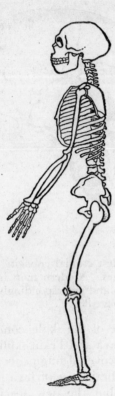

NEANDERTHAL   HOMO SAPIENS

NEANDERTHAL MAN

The men of Java and Pekin may have lived about half-a-million years ago, mid-way through the Pleistocene period. Human fossils which can be assigned to the early part of the Pleistocene are fragmentary and difficult to interpret. We must therefore now come to the Upper Pleistocene. During a great part of this period most of the old world seems to have been inhabited by a variety of man that regularly buried his dead. Like some American Indians and the Ainus today, he also left in the graves tools and sometimes animal skulls. We thus have large numbers of well preserved specimens, together with the tools they used and the remains of animals they hunted.

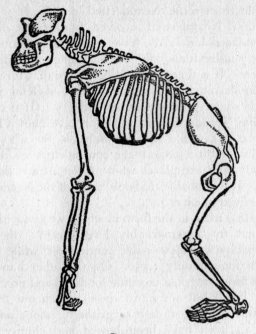

GORILLA

SKELETONS

In skeletal structure we (*Homo sapiens*) show full modification for walking upright on two legs. Gorilla is not adapted for walking, but has very long arms suitable for "brachiation" in trees. *H. Neanderthalensis* is more ape-like than we are—a feature which he evidently developed anew, since earlier human and prehuman types walked erect as we do

These men have from the first been classified as belonging to the same genus, *Homo*, as ourselves : their Latin name is *Homo Neanderthalensis*, from the place in Germany in which many skeletons were discovered. Neanderthal man occupied the whole of Europe and North Africa, and similar remains have been found in Central Africa (Rhodesian man) and Java (Solo man).

The limbs of the Rhodesian and Solo types, like those of *Homo erectus* (=*Pithecanthropus*), resemble ours. Moreover, some of the *Homo erectus* skulls from Pekin are almost indistinguishable from some Neanderthal skulls. It is therefore thought that Neanderthal evolved from *Homo erectus*, and perhaps replaced him. We have complete skeletons of more than twenty individuals, and the incomplete remains of very many others. It is therefore possible to see that this species of man, like modern man, was very variable in skeletal characters: the Neanderthal type is not at all uniform. (It is commonly believed that Neanderthal man lived in caves, but it is perhaps more correct to say that it is the archæologists who have the cave-dwelling habit : caves make convenient sites for archæological study, and are places where skeletons are likely to be preserved. It is probable that only a few of the Neanderthalers themselves lived in caves.)

Neanderthal man, in the form in which we know him best, is distinguished by a remarkably large brain : the average cranial capacity was 1,450 cubic centimetres, while the figure for modern man is only 1,350. On the other hand he had prominent brow ridges, a receding forehead and no chin. The teeth were larger but not more ape-like than our own. The general skeleton was, rather surprisingly, more anthropoid, and the gait must have been bowed and clumsy. This is surprising because the earlier men of Java and Pekin had body skeletons like our own. The average height was about five feet.

Neanderthal man, compared with modern man, was not very enterprising in his use of stone tools. He flaked stone to make scrapers and pointed implements, and simple bone tools were also used. The stone-age culture for which he was responsible was the Mousterian. He seems to have hunted mainly by means of fall-traps. There are no cave drawings associated with Neanderthal man.

It has been held that Neanderthal was no more than a cousin of modern man : that he evolved quite separately from our own ancestors, spread over a large part of the world, and was later replaced by *Homo sapiens*. This view is supported by the fact that the early Neanderthalers are more like ourselves than the later ones : this is evidence of evolutionary divergence from our own line. Moreover, in Europe the Neanderthal communities were quite suddenly replaced by men of modern type, evidently as a result of immigration by the latter. As we dig down we find first the comparatively recent traces of *H. sapiens*, and then, quite abruptly, an earlier deposit with Neanderthal remains. There was no gradual change from one type to the other.

This view of the later Neanderthal men, as sharply distinct from ourselves, may have to be modified as a result of some remarkable discoveries in caves on Mount Carmel, in Palestine. In one cave was found the skeleton of a woman, mainly Neanderthal in structure but with some modern features. In another there were several skeletons, of modern type on the whole but with some Neanderthal characteristics. One explanation of these discoveries is that on Mount Carmel (and doubtless elsewhere) men of modern type were mingling with Neanderthalers, and breeding with them, just as widely divergent human types intermarry today when emigration brings them together. The two types had doubtless evolved separately whilst parted by geographical barriers ; but they were not so different when they met that they could not interbreed.

This interpretation is only a suggestion, and we shall need many more discoveries of fossil men before everyone is satisfied. Nevertheless we can regard the Mount Carmel discoveries, tentatively, as the last stage in the series that ends with modern man. If we recapitulate we see that the chain is weakest at the beginning. The nearest we have to apes ancestral both to ourselves and to modern apes are *Dryopithecus* and other Miocene types such as *Proconsul* ; our knowledge of these genera resembles the fossils themselves in being only fragmentary. The next stage is that of the South African man-apes, which had already acquired the type of skeleton needed for walking upright ; but they had ape-like skulls and correspondingly small brains. Then we come to the earliest individuals known to have made tools. The men of Java and Pekin not only walked erect, but also had larger brains and more human skulls than the man-apes. Pekin man grades off into Neanderthal man, and, as we have just seen, there are intermediates also between early Neanderthal and ourselves. The later Neanderthalers diverged greatly from our own type, and were finally displaced by us throughout the world.

7

UNSOLVED PROBLEMS

It would be convenient if the story of human evolution could be left in the form summarised in the last paragraph, but unfortunately there are some enigmatic fragments which quite fail to fit comfortably into any simple scheme. Two of them have especial fame and interest, and will be described here.

The first is the *Swanscombe skull*. This skull is known from two fragments, forming the back and base of the cranium and part of one side. They were found in a gravel pit south of the Thames between Dartford and Gravesend. Howells, the American anthropologist, remarks on the geological appeal of the district, and refers to

> the perils of any navvy who works there : the back of his neck is hot from the breath of archæologists, and he can hardly throw a shovelful of gravel in any direction without hitting some tweedy individual from a learned society.

The Swanscombe skull belonged to a woman in her early twenties. Her skull bones were thicker than is usual in modern skulls, but her cranial capacity seems to have been 1,325 to 1,350 cubic centimetres. Her importance is that she was almost certainly a contemporary of Java and Pekin man, and so provides fairly convincing evidence for the existence of men of modern appearance in the middle Pleistocene.

It is obvious that we shall be unable to interpret these remains finally until we have many more specimens. There is some further fragmentary evidence of the existence of *sapiens*-like individuals in the Middle Pleistocene, before the appearance of Neanderthal man. The Steinheim skull is one : this is another woman, possibly rather like the Swanscombe specimen but also with some Neanderthal features. In time she comes later than Swanscombe, but earlier than Neanderthal. This applies also to yet a further fragment, found in the Charente district of France, and briefly described in 1949 ; again the bones are unusually thick, but otherwise of modern appearance and without Neanderthal features.

The other remarkable but isolated fossil is the *Piltdown man*, also called the Sussex woman on account of the probable sex of the original owner of the skull. This fossil was found accidentally in a gravel pit. The cranium, or brain-case, resembles that of modern man in general form, but the bones are twice as thick. The size of the brain was probably near the average for modern man : about 1,350 cubic centimetres ; but several different estimates have been made. There are two things about this fossil that have led to discussion and controversy. One is that a lower jaw bone was found near it, in circumstances that suggest that the two fragments belonged to the same individual. This jaw bone is of rather light construction, unlike the cranium, and in form it is ape-like, without a chin. Many authorities have therefore accepted that the Sussex woman had a skull for the most part resembling ours, though heavier, but a jaw like that of an ape. This is not impossible on theoretical grounds, but it proved too much for some archæologists to swallow ; these sceptics asserted that the jaw must have been part of some quite different individual.

The other aspect of the Sussex woman which has caused discussion is her age. She has been held to belong to the Middle Pleistocene, and so to be roughly contemporary with the men of Java and Pekin. However, as this book goes to press it is reported that chemical analysis of fragments of both cranium and lower jaw indicate that their age is 100,000 years or less.

For the non-specialist the most obvious significance of these obscure remains is that when many more fossils have been found the evolution of modern man and his near relatives is likely to present a rather complex picture in time and space. It seems likely that from the Miocene onwards a great variety of prehuman and human types have appeared in different parts of the world, and their precise relationships with each other will be unravelled only when much more evidence is available.

Modern Man

Our own type, for which the name *Homo sapiens* is usually reserved, has spread and multiplied over the whole world within the past 70,000 years. In our bony structure the distinctive features include the relative lightness of the bones, brow-ridges which form no more than a pair of small bumps in the forehead, hollow cheeks, a well-developed chin and a prominent nose. The last two features are related to the disappearance of a projecting snout : without the development of a prominent nose this would have left rather little room for the nasal cavity ; similarly the tongue muscles would have had to be very small but for the change in the shape of the lower jaw that gives us our chins.

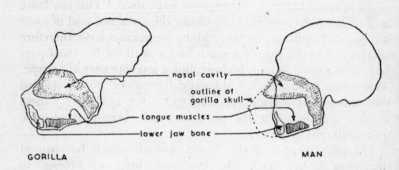

GORILLA   MAN

NOSE AND CHIN

Outlines of skulls of gorilla (left) and man (right), with nasal cavities and tongue muscles shaded. In man the projecting nose allows the same amount of nasal cavity as in a gorilla ; and the thickness of the lower jaw bone is on the outside in man, giving him a chin and making room for the tongue muscles

As for our teeth, we have a better record of the modifications they have undergone than of any other structure. There is an unbroken series of teeth, modern or fossil, from the completely ape to the human. We have lost both the canine tusk and the cheek teeth adapted for tearing flesh with a shear-like action ; and in general our teeth are relatively small and close together. It has been suggested that the reduction in the size of the canines, and the modification of the molars for grinding only, may have taken place during a period when our ancestors were of great size, or at least had very heavy skeletons. Men of sufficient size or weight would probably have had teeth large enough to tear flesh without special modification. We are probably now undergoing evolutionary change in the direction of fewer teeth : some people fail to develop the normal number of wisdom teeth, and this is evidently related to the overcrowding of the teeth that has resulted from reduction of the snout. Our own teeth today are capable of dealing with a varied, but not a very tough, diet. Man is, in fact, capable of living on a far wider range of foods than most mammals : omnivorous behaviour such as we display is hardly found elsewhere except among the rats and mice that share our food.

Our hairlessness also may be a result of large size. Large mammals lose heat from the body surface less easily than small ones, since the greater their size the smaller is the ratio of surface area to volume ; they are thus less likely to require hair to keep them warm. Just as elephants and other large mammals are relatively hairless it may be that our ancestors lost their hair, as a result of an evolutionary process, when they were of great size. Today our hairless condition, like the structure of our teeth, makes us more adaptable : by varying our clothes we can tolerate an exceptionally wide range of climates. Few, if any, other animal species are as widely spread over the earth as *Homo sapiens*.

But our adaptability is, more than anything else, related to the remarkable nature of our limbs and brains. The way we move about is very unusual. The apes are exceptional in having an upright position whilst moving. This is related to the trapese method of locomotion, a mode of locomotion which is most highly developed today in the gibbon, with its long arms and small legs. In men, though the arms are long for a mammal, they are shorter than in most apes, and our legs are relatively very long : in us the physique of the upright apes has been converted for walking. It is believed that our ape ancestors developed the ground-living habit when climatic changes brought a reduction in the areas covered by forests : over a long period the forests thinned out, giving place to larger and larger grass-covered clearings. This is in line with what we know of the way in which other modes of locomotion, such as that of the hoofed mammals, evolved. The Miocene ape, Proconsul, described earlier, may represent this stage in human development.

Walking upright requires more than an enlargement of the legs. The curve of the vertebral column alters so that we are not bowed when walking as an ape is. There are also important changes in the foot. The human big toe is non-opposable : that is, we cannot use it in grasping objects as we use our thumb and as apes use both thumb and big toe. (It has been remarked that man has two hands but apes have four.) We still have vestiges of the muscles used for working the big toe as a thumb. Together with the reduction in the functions of the toes the mechanical arrangement of the bones of the foot is changed. Apes have a highly flexible foot, without a well-marked heel. In ours there are two fixed arches, which enable us to rise on our toes, and a well developed heel. We are thus able to stride and to run. An ape's movement on the ground is limited much as ours is if we walk only on our heels without using the ball of the foot.

The use of the legs alone for walking, and of the arms and hands alone for other purposes, has meant a great deal in the development of man. When the walking habit evolved our ancestors had probably already a highly developed co-ordination of movements of the hands with sight : this had been necessary for movement in the trees. With the hands released from locomotory function the hand-eye relationship came to have other uses. Hands could be used more and more for manipulation. (All these changes took place over an immensely long period—probably several million years. There was no deliberate choice, by our ancestors, of the use to which they put their limbs. They were undergoing the slow process of evolutionary change which was discussed at the beginning of this chapter.)

In most mammals the snout is the first part of the body that comes in contact with an object, and smell is one of the most important of the senses, usually much more important than sight. In man the hands have come to be the exploratory organs ; we have no snout, our sense of smell is less acute, but our eyesight is exceptionally good. Many of our most important peculiarities, such as our eyes, our ability to breed at any season and the muscles which enable us to make facial movements expressing emotion, are shared with the modern

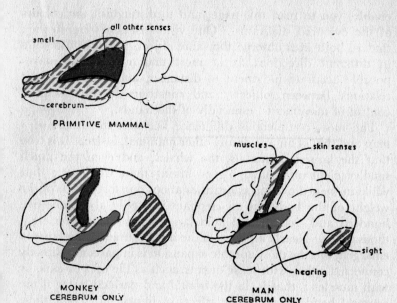

THREE BRAINS

Not only is the human brain relatively and absolutely far larger than the others, but it is more complex, and large parts of the cerebrum (not shaded) are concerned with "higher" mental processes. The drawings are not to the same scale (see page 93)

apes. But apes have no *speech*. Our ability to make complex sounds, and to use them to refer both to objects or processes and to ideas, is unique in nature, and with our manual dexterity makes human society possible. (The dominance of the sense of sight, by contrast with smell, we share with all the primates— the apes, monkeys and lemurs.) All these changes were accompanied by corresponding changes in the structure of the brain. The part concerned with smell became much reduced, that with sight enlarged. Like the monkeys, but not other mammals, we have a specially sensitive area, the macula, near the middle of the retina of the eye ; it is this area which enables you to read this page, and to distinguish the colours of the coloured diagrams. Our vision is also stereoscopic : that is, both eyes observe the same object, instead of looking in different directions as in most mammals ; this makes possible accurate judgment of distances, and of the spatial relations between objects, and consequently the accurate control of movements, especially of the hands.

The most conspicuous difference between the brain of a man and that of an ape or any other mammal, is size. It is true that the largest mammals, the whales, and even the much smaller elephants, have bigger brains than we have ; but while in man the brain constitutes about one forty-sixth of the weight of the body, in an elephant it is only about one five hundred and sixtieth and in a large whale about one eight thousandth. Nearly all parts of the human brain are relatively enlarged, but the most notable expansion is in parts not directly connected either with sense organs, such as the eyes or ears, or with muscles ; that is, in the frontal and parietal parts of the cerebral hemispheres. The effects of injury show that these regions are particularly concerned with the capacity to perform very complex tasks which involve the solution of problems, and with memory.

There is much variation of brain size among individuals : while the average cranial capacity for males is between 1,300 and 1,500 cubic centimetres, normal individuals range from 1,050 to 1,800. It might be thought that a relation could be found between brain size and intelligence, but this is not the case ; if it were, Eskimos would be the people with the highest average intelligence, since they have the largest brains. Moreover Neanderthal man, who seems to have had no art and who created only primitive stone tools, had a higher cranial capacity than we have. Knowledge of the internal structure of his brain might suggest a reason for his ultimate replacement by modern man. Certainly, together with size, the human brain has developed a very great complexity of microscopic structure, giving scope for much variation that could not be detected from an examination of externals.

This account of human evolution has treated of man as an animal, albeit an exceptional one. The picture so far is of an upright, hairless, ground-living ape, with a swollen head and brain, no snout, rather feeble teeth, a reduced sense of smell, excellent eye-sight, remarkable dexterity, and the power of speech. These characters make possible the other unique features of man which are usually considered to be the foundation of his humanity. These other features are those which make man a social animal, and in chapter 10 we shall continue this account of man with a description of human society.

HUMAN TYPES

The world in all doth but two nations bear,
The good, the bad, and these mixed everywhere.
ANDREW MARVELL

THIS chapter is largely about trivialities to which an unjusti-
fied importance has been attached. It deals with the relatively
minor physical differences found in the human species today,
and particularly with those, such as skin colour, which have a
well-marked geographical distribution.

THE RACES OF MAN

It is usual to divide the human species into three main
groups distinguished primarily by the structure of their hair.
The *Negroids* have woolly hair and broad noses ; they
include Bantu-speaking Africans, the South African Bushmen,
the negroes of West Africa, the pigmy Negritoes of Malaysia
and Africa, the Andamanese and Melanesians. The Negroids
are very variable in other physical characteristics : they may
be black, brown or yellow ; their jaws may be prognathous
(projecting) or not ; and their skulls may be broad or narrow
although most of them have narrow skulls.

The second group, the *Caucasoids,* or Caucasians, have wavy
hair and narrow noses. They inhabit Europe, the Mediterranean countries, Asia Minor and India ; they are also, as a
result of recent emigration, the main inhabitants of North
America. The Ainus of Japan are Caucasoid, but in respects
other than hair and nose shape resemble their mongoloid
neighbours. The Caucasoids may have white or brown skins,
and broad or narrow skulls.

The third group, the *Mongoloids,* have lank, straight hair ;
their noses are intermediate in width. They include most of
the inhabitants of Asia, apart from India, and the indigenous
peoples of the Americas from the Eskimos of the north to the
Fuegans in the south. Their skulls are for the most part
broad.

94

There is a fourth, very small group, which does not fit into the three main ones. The *Australoids* (that is to say, the original native inhabitants of Australia—the aborigines or bushmen) have wavy, Caucasoid hair, but broad noses like those of Negroids. Their skin is as dark as that of negroes, but this may well be the product of a separate evolutionary development. It seems quite likely that the Australoids have been almost or quite isolated from other human groups for a very large part of the time during which modern man has existed, and some anthropologists believe them to be the most primitive of human types ; that is, they are considered to resemble most closely the common ancestors of all present-day men. Their average cranial capacity is 1,250 cubic centimetres, which is below the average for man as a whole ; the head bones are thicker, and the teeth rather large. However, some authorities believe the Australoids to be derived from a mixture of two or more human types which had come together as a result of emigration. Nothing conclusive can be said on the precise status or significance of the Australoids.

The question is often asked, which of the three main groups is the most primitive ? and the answer is sometimes supposed to be that the Negroids are primitive, because, on the whole, they have not developed such advanced societies as have the Mongoloids and Caucasoids. But if we consider anatomical features (and the three "races" are defined anatomically) we find that things are not so simple. We first have to decide what we mean by "primitive", since it is easy, but unprofitable, to use the word as an undefined term of derogation. In biology one type is said to be more primitive than another when it is regarded as the more similar to a common ancestor of both types. Since the ancestors of man were apes it seems to follow that primitive men are those that are most ape-like. But we know very little of the structure of the apes from which both men and present-day apes are sprung, apart from their skeletons, and so comparison is often made between man and his nearest contemporary relatives, the chimpanzee and gorilla. These of course have undergone evolutionary change, just as man has, during the last few million years, and so are not a reliable guide to what is primitive. And if we make the comparison we find no clear picture. The Caucasoids are ape-like in having a good deal of hair on their bodies, in having wavy hair, and in their thin lips ; on the other hand in the formation of the face they are least ape-like. The Negroids are ape-like in their broad noses, but less ape-like than Caucasoids in their thick lips and the structure and distribution of the hair. It is evident that no definite statement can be made on which of the main human groups is anatomically primitive. Men and women of the four types described can and do inter-marry and produce offspring of mixed characteristics without any difficulty apart from social barriers. Consequently, wherever there are mixed populations intermediates are found.

This applies even more obviously when we come to study the sub-divisions of the three principal groups. It is customary among anthropologists to classify the whole of the human species in about thirty divisions. They will not be described here. However, owing to the political implications that have been given to the term "nordic" the European types are worth a mention.

It is usual to describe three main European types. The *Mediterranean* type is described by Huxley & Haddon as having :

> . . . an average stature of about 5 feet 3 inches, slender build, long head and narrow oval face, straight nose rather inclining to be broad ; the eyes are very dark.

This type is represented throughout Europe, especially in the west, and also in North Africa (where its representatives are called Hamites). The Semites, that is, the peoples such as the Arabs and the original, Palestinian Jews, who speak semitic languages, include a large proportion of individuals of the Mediterranean type.

A second type, the *Alpine*, the same authors describe as :

> . . . very broad-headed, [with] chestnut brown or black hair, hazel-grey or brown eyes. The nose is inclined to be broad and is frequently concave. The stature is medium, about 5 feet 4½ inches, and the body is thick-set. The range of this type is from Russia to central France. The Eastern members are termed Slavs.

(There are three other types closely similar to the Alpine :

the Iranian, "prevalent from Persia to Manchuria", with an "abundance of facial hair" ; the Armenoid of the near East, "of medium-stature, stocky and fleshy" with a prominent, aquiline nose ; and the Dinaric or Illyrian of the northern Adriatic region, which is "characterised by pronounced brachycephaly [broad-headedness], tall stature, dark hair, rather tawny skin, long face, and particularly by the long, narrow, high-bridged, convex nose.")

For the third European main type, the *Nordic*, the description is :

> . . . florid or reddish-white skin, straight, wavy or curly hair of a yellow, light brown or tawny colour ; typically the eyes are blue or grey. The head is mesocephalic with a tendency to dolicocephaly [of medium width with a tendency to narrowness] ; . . . the face is long with a prominent, narrow, usually straight nose and a well-developed chin. This is the characteristic type of Scandinavia, it is also common in the north central European plain and frequent in the British Isles.

It will be noticed that the descriptions are rather vague. Moreover use is made not only of differences which are largely or entirely independent of environment (such as those of eye colour), but also of some known to be much influenced by environment, such as stature. This is characteristic of definitions in physical anthropology, whether what is defined is called a race, an ethnic group, a regional group or simply a type. The reason for the use of the word type in this book is that it is unambiguous ; it is quite legitimate, even if rather pointless, to speak of a nordic type, for instance, provided that "nordic" is fully defined. There is then no difficulty in deciding whether any particular individual belongs to the nordic type or not.

Almost any European can, by looking at the people he meets every day, see that intermediates exist between the three types just described. Nevertheless it might be true that in any given part of the continent a majority of the people belong to one type. It is, indeed, easy to get this impression from some anthropological writings. However, investigation shows that the impression is misleading. In one instance 250 Swiss soldiers, from German-speaking cantons, were studied. None was found to have the combination of height, narrow-headedness, light eyes and blond hair of the nordic type ; 9.2 per cent had the Alpine combination of characters ; 0.8 per cent had the Dinaric combination ; and 0.4 per cent that of the Mediterranean. Thus only 26 of them, or 10.4 per cent, belonged to one of the anthropological types, and the remaining 224 showed a mixture of characters. Even in Sweden, which has the highest proportion of nordics, army recruits in 1897-8 were found to include only 11 per cent of the nordic type.

Not only are there no populations in Europe today of which most of the members are of one type ; there is no reason to think that there ever were such populations. The existence of a good deal of variation within the various species of fossil man was mentioned in chapter 4. When a group of human fossils is found in one place, and belonging to the same period, whether of our own or another species, the degree of variation in the skeletons is similar to that found in the mixed populations of today.

The existence of a great deal of variation in human populations is clearly very important. Some aspects of it were discussed in chapters 2 and 3, and others will appear in the next two chapters. We have seen that this variation is due partly to differences in genetic constitution, and that each individual has a unique combination of genes. If we consider characteristics that are largely independent of environment we find that every possible combination of them exists. Thus blue eyes can appear with both dark and fair hair, negroid hair with a fair skin, and so on. Different combinations are, indeed, found in members of the same family : when both parents are European one child may approximate to the nordic type and another to the alpine. It is because of this occurrence of many different combinations of characters that man was classified above primarily on the basis of hair structure, since this is a single character of which the development is not significantly influenced by change of environment. In defining the negroid, caucasoid and mongoloid types it was also possible to use the shape of the nose, since the distribution of the different nasal types coincides, on the whole, with that of the hair types. The exceptions to this rule are found where there has been intermarriage between members of these groups ; and in the Australoids, with their combination of caucasoid hair and negroid nostrils.

ANATOMICAL DIFFERENCES

Many of the general points which have arisen in the preceding paragraphs can be illustrated by considering in more detail some of the physical features in which men differ. The anatomical features which differentiate human groups are nearly all superficial in the most literal sense : that is, they are external features. A distinguished anatomist has pointed out that if the bodies of say a negro and a European were both flayed, so that skin and hair were removed and the face obliterated, it would be impossible to tell for certain which was which. "Racial" differences, it has been said, are only skin deep.

The most obvious of these differences is in *skin colour*. The colour of a man's skin is determined by three things : first the amount it contains of a black pigment called melanin ; second the outer layer of dead cells, which varies in thickness ; and third the blood in the vessels below the surface. Melanin is the only substance responsible for the major differences of colour between the natives of different parts of the world : there are no different black, brown and yellow pigments, and the many different shades are due to the combined effects of the three factors just mentioned. People of northern countries would have very nearly white skins, instead of pink, but for the effect of the blood ; this whiteness can be seen in an anæmic person, or in one who has lost much blood. It is not due to a white substance in the skin, any more than is the whiteness of a cloud or a mist, but to the scattering of light by the surface cells. Some black pigment is present in the skins even of the palest people. The only exceptions are albinos, who typically have no pigment in the skin, hair or iris of the eye. (They consequently have pink eyes, since the blood shows through.) Albinism is a rare condition which may occur in any human group, including those with the darkest skins ; it is due to a recessive gene like that responsible for red hair.

In general, the greater the amount of strong sunlight in a

country the darker the native inhabitants are found to be. The main exception is in the American Indians, who are all rather similar in colour from Alaska in the north to Tierra del Fuego in the south ; but these men are in America as a result of a relatively recent immigration, of less than ten thousand years ago, and so presumably retain the hue of their nomadic ancestors.

The dark skin of a negro is not due to the *direct* effects of the sun : negroes have the capacity to form melanin in their skin without exposure to the sun. This capacity varies in a fairly regular way in different groups of men between the poles and equator, and the differences between individuals in this respect are clearly genetical in origin. (The capacity to respond to sun-light by melanin formation, as when we go brown in summer, also varies, but that is a separate point.) It is possible that the dark skin of tropical peoples is a product of natural selection, since it gives protection against sunburn. In view of this biolog-ical usefulness (or *survival value*) of very dark pigmentation it is quite likely that it has been evolved separately in different human groups inhabiting different tropical areas. Certainly the genes which are especially concerned with melanin formation are differ-ent in different groups: in west African negroes they are numerous, but in the dark Bantu-speaking Africans only two or three genes are involved. Hence the results of crossing with whites are different in the two cases.

Colour variation is of course familiar in other species, and particularly in domestic animals. Haldane has pointed out that race horses vary a great deal in colour, and that there is no connexion between their colour and desirable qualities such as the ability to win races. As we shall see in the next chapter, there is a parallel here with man.

The next obvious external feature is *hair*. Human hair varies in structure, colour, and distribution on the body. The essential difference between negroid, caucasoid and mongol-oid hair is the shape of each individual hair. Within the first two types there is a good deal of variation : the Papuans and Melanesians have long hair, negroes have short, woolly hair, and bushmen very short, tightly coiled hair. Similarly, caucasoid hair may be almost straight or quite curly. What-

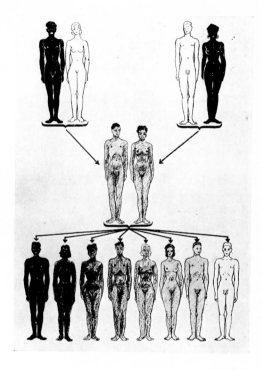

PLATE 5

NEGRO-WHITE CROSSING

The result of crossing between whites and West African negroids, shown diagrammatically : many genes are involved in the determination of colour, and the second generation has a great variety of types. Compare the next plate

PLATE 6

NEGRO-WHITE CROSSING

A result of crossing between white and South African negroids. Few genes are involved in colour determination, and so a "black" can have a "white" child or conversely. Here the mother is an English-Basuto half-breed who married a white man. "Whites" of mixed origin in South Africa are often not acknowledged by their darker relatives, so that they can have the privileges which go with a white skin

NEGROID
A Zulu of South Africa

PLATE 7

PLATE 8

CAUCASOID

An Arab of North Africa

MONGOLOID

Dakota of North America

ever the structure of hair its usual colour is black, and only among some European peoples are there many exceptions to this rule. The pigment responsible is the same melanin as that found in the skin. Red hair, however, has a special pigment; it turns up here and there throughout Europe and western Asia, but is especially common among the Irish and Welsh, the Scottish highlanders, and among Jews and Finns. As for the distribution of hair on the body, caucasoids tend to have most body hair, and negroids least. Hair differences seem to have no such biological value as skin colour has, and there is no satisfactory explanation of their existence. Apart from the temporary effects of permanent waving (or straightening in negro women), environmental influences have little or no effect.

Other facial characteristics can be dealt with very shortly. *Eye colour*, that is the colour of the iris, is generally brown or black, but where the skin and hair are lightly pigmented blue, grey and green eyes are quite common. It is however possible for dark people to have grey or blue eyes, and for blonds to have dark eyes. The function of the iris pigment is probably to protect the interior of the eye from the harmful effects of sunlight ; consequently light-eyed people are at a disadvantage in sunny countries, and are commonly obliged to wear dark glasses.

Eye form varies owing to differences in the arrangement of the skin round the eyes. Mongoloids tend to have "slit eyes", and some, particularly in Asia, have the "epicanthic fold", a fold of skin that covers the inner angle of the eye. This fold can occur in negroids and caucasoids, but in them it is rare.

As for *nasal form*, the flat, broad type of nose (platyrrhine) is probably primitive. It seems likely that the leptorrhine, or narrow-nosed condition is a result of natural selection : in general, the hotter and moister the air, the broader the noses of the native inhabitants ; in colder climates it may be an advantage to have a high, narrow nose in which the air is warmed before it reaches the lungs.

We come now to a feature to which anthropologists have attached greater importance than to any other : this is *head form*. There are many ways in which the human head varies, including the flatness of the face and the degree of projection

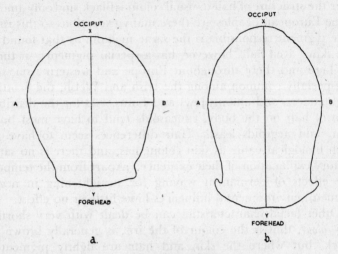

CEPHALIC INDEX

Outlines of skulls seen from above : (a) brachycephalic, (b) dolico-cephalic. In each the CI is obtained by dividing the length of AB by the length of XY, and multiplying by 100

of the jaws (prognathism) ; but the character most studied is the ratio between the maximum width and the maximum length. This can be measured in a living person, and is then called the cephalic index ; in a skull it is called the cranial index ; for each the abbreviation CI is used. If the maximum width is x and the maximum length y, the CI is

$$\frac{\text{x.100}}{\text{y}}$$

On this basis heads are classified in three groups :

CI over 80 : brachycephalic (head relatively short or broad) ;

CI from 75 to 80 : mesocephalic (intermediate) ;

CI under 75 : dolicocephalic (head relatively long or narrow).

The classification is quite arbitrary, and the selection of figures a matter of convenience. The index gives no indication of the extent to which the front, middle or rear parts of the skull make up its total length, or of which part is widest. Consequently skulls of the same CI may be different in shape as a whole.

The broadest heads are found among mongoloids, the narrowest among negroids. Some Asiatic groups average 86.8, and one west African people 71.8. European averages vary a great deal. It is a curious fact that central Europeans, including Germans, are decidedly brachycephalic (a non-nordic characteristic) ; in the north, in Britain and in Spain averages are mostly between 76 and 79. However, in every European population, and indeed in most populations throughout the world, there is great variation, and some people are decidedly narrow, others broadheaded.

Head shape is influenced by environment. This has been most clearly established in experiments on laboratory animals : some vitamin deficiencies induce in rats a more dolicocephalic skull form ; domesticated wolves have much more brachycephalic skulls than wild ones. In some human groups it appears that head form is slightly correlated with stature, so that the taller the individual the more dolicocephalic he is likely to be. Since height is very much influenced by nutrition it follows that an improved diet may lead to narrower heads— the opposite effect from that in rats. It has also been suggested that head shape may be influenced by the position in which a baby sleeps, and the softness of its pillow or mattress. However, the extent to which this effect actually occurs is not certain.

There is a great deal still to be learnt about the influence of environmental factors, such as nutrition and possibly climate, on head shape, on other skeletal characters and indeed on bodily form in general. This is illustrated by some remarkable observations on change of skull shape among the families of immigrants to the United States. For example, Sicilian males born in Sicily have an average CI of 77.7 ; those born in the United States, 81.5. On the other hand Jewish males become less brachycephalic in America, from 83.0 to 81.4. The changes among females are similar but smaller. The comment of Boas, the anthropologist who discovered these changes, is that "all the evidence is now in favour of a great plasticity of human types".

This conclusion is supported by the study of *stature* in

different human groups. The tallest men are the negroes of the Sudan and the Lake Chad region in Central Africa, the shortest the negritoes, also of Central Africa, with an average height of only 4 feet 6 inches. But nearly every group shows great variation among its members. In chapter 8 we shall see that this variation is partly due to differences of environment, as well as genetical differences, within each nation. For the present we are concerned with the characteristics of whole communities. For instance, the Japanese are commonly regarded as a "short race". Certainly the average height of Japanese adults in Japan is less than that of Europeans or Americans, but to speak of them as a short *race* suggests that their stature is determined genetically and is consequently unalterable, except possibly by selection during many centuries. This is not the case. The children of Japanese emigrants to the United States or Hawaii are a good deal taller, on the average, than children in Japan itself : for boys of 15 years the difference is about 10 cm. Chinese show similar differences. Probably they are due largely to improved diet.

The importance of food is illustrated by experiments in which the diets of various Indian groups were fed to rats. The rats, which were all genetically similar, reflected in a remarkable way certain of the characteristics of the group whose diet they received. Thus the Pathans are physically impressive, and the rats fed on their national diet were large, developed very little disease, had large litters, and had a low infant and maternal mortality. Madrassis, at the other extreme, are physically much inferior ; rats fed with their diet (largely rice) were small, had poor coats, much disease, small litters and high death rates. Thus some of the so-called racial differences between Indian nationalities are probably due to dietary differences.

We shall refer to similar experiments in chapter 12. Meanwhile, if we turn from stature to *body-build* we find that there is less information on what determines it, but what there is reinforces the impression gained from the study of cephalic index and stature. Every kind of body-build is found in almost every human community, though the proportion that each type makes of the total may vary. There is also evidence that, as would be expected, environment may influence body-build. Both in the United States and Japan it has been found that there are more tall, slender individuals among the rich. It has also been claimed that peasants and farm labourers tend to the opposite type. These facts—if they are facts—have been attributed to environmental influences, including differences in nutrition and in occupation. But very much more work is required before we can reach any definite conclusion.

There is little satisfactory evidence that particular temperaments are regularly associated with particular physiques. "Let me have men about me that are fat", said Cæsar,

> Yond Cassius has a lean and hungry look ;
> He thinks too much : such men are dangerous.

But it is doubtful if he was justified. It can however be said that certain physical types are more liable to some types of mental instability than others.

The attempt has been made to relate physical differences between human groups to glandular function. A change in the functioning of the system of endocrine or ductless glands can produce drastic physical and mental changes : for instance, thyroid deficiency causes cretinism, abnormality of the pituitary gland may cause giantism, and, as we have seen, several endocrine glands influence sexual development and behaviour. There is however no evidence that, for example, pigmies are of small stature owing to thyroid deficiency, or that the tall, slender negroes of the Nile region owe their physique to a subnormal production of the sex hormones.

One physiological characteristic occupies a special position : the existence of different types of blood is familiar from its importance in blood transfusion, and it is well known that every individual is a member of one of four *blood groups*. Today it is known that the blood of individuals varies in a large number of ways, and at least 2,560 kinds of human blood can now be distinguished. The four best known types have been studied extensively from an anthropological point of view. The four groups are called respectively O, A, B and AB. They are determined genetically in a quite simple way, and no environmental effect is known to influence them. It is found that all four groups occur in every human group, but that the proportions vary. To quote Weidenreich :

> In the Eskimo or North American Indians the overwhelming majority of individuals belong to the O group. Among the Argentines, Bantu Negroes, Australian aborigines, Germans from the Eifel, and the Mongolian Giliaks of Sakhalin, the O individuals are in predominance and show about the same frequency in each group. In Koreans, Australians, and Egyptians the percentage of A individuals is the same, but not that of the B individuals, who are, however, equally frequent in Dravidians, Koreans, Egyptians, and the Ainus of Japan.
>
> Unquestionably, mankind can be classified . . . according to the frequency of the blood qualities; but these . . . groups are not identical with those obtained by the customary anthropological methods, nor is there any correlation between them.

What is "Race" ?

The facts of variation in physical characters are certainly confusing, especially since it is usual to speak of human groups as if they were sharply marked off and distinct from each other. We now find that for the most part they are not sharply marked off ; that physical features can occur in any combination ; and that some of these features are influenced by environment and may be conspicuously altered in one or two generations. When this point is reached the question may be asked : what then is race ? This question presupposes that, because there is a word *race*, there must be something corresponding to it— something of which it is the name. This is very far from being the case. If you look in a dictionary you find a large number of different meanings for the term race, and if you look in the writings, not only of laymen but also of experts, you may find it difficult or impossible to make out which meaning the term is supposed to have.

However, most people have something fairly definite in mind when they speak of races. They may think of human groups relatively well marked off from each other, such as negroes and Europeans (ignoring, for convenience, the existence of intermediates due to intermarriage). Or they may think of differences such as those between Scots and Greeks, although in this case there is a great deal of overlap and the distinction is one of averages : for instance, the average degree of skin pigmentation, or the proportion of blue-eyed individuals. And sometimes they may even think of national, or cultural characters. Always, however, or nearly always, the characters are thought of as innate—as genetically determined and un-alterable by environmental changes. We have already seen to what extent physical differences are independent of environ-ment, and in the next chapter differences in behaviour, or psychological differences, will be considered.

Meanwhile it is possible to give a reasonable definition for the word race, so that if the term must be used at all it can be used precisely. A race may be defined as a group which shares in common a certain set of genes, and which became distinct from other groups as a result of geographical isolation. The possession of genes in common is not alone sufficient to qualify a particular group as a race : no biologist would speak of the race of albinos, for example, or the race of red-haired people. Races in our sense arise as a result of isolation from other groups, and this fact is included in the definition. A definition of this sort, though fairly precise, is not much help in the study of human differences. It is useful mainly in avoid-ing the errors that come from the use of a term that is undefined, or has a number of different and incompatible meanings. These errors are the more likely to arise when, as with race, the term is often used to arouse emotion rather than to give information. In fact, the question "what is race ? " is not a very profitable one to ask. The question that we are concerned to answer in this book is : what are the *facts* about human diversity ? In this chapter we have outlined the facts of physical diversity ; in the next we turn to differences of behaviour.

CHAPTER 7

RACE THEORY

Of all the vulgar modes of escaping from the
consideration of the effect of social and moral
influences upon the human mind, the most
vulgar is that of attributing the diversities of
conduct and character to inherent natural
differences.

JOHN STUART MILL

IT is quite obvious that most of the physical qualities discussed
in the last chapter have little or no direct social importance.
A man's physique may qualify him for some types of work, and
disqualify him for others, but the shape of his head or the
amount of melanin in his skin are not likely to be considered by
a foreman recruiting stevedores, nor by the examiners for a
medical degree. Most people, if they had to make a list of the
socially desirable qualities, would no doubt suggest some of
the following : emotional stability ; health and energy ;
intelligence and initiative ; moral behaviour. They would not
include any particular eye-colour or nose shape. Some,
however, if the point were raised, might assert that there is a
connexion between, say, skin pigment and moral behaviour :
for example Lombroso describes the Negro as follows :

The principal thing is always . . . the stifling of the
primitive. Even if he is dressed in the European way and
has accepted the customs of modern culture, all too often
there remains in him the lack of respect for the life of his
fellow men, the disregard for life which all wild people have
in common. To them, a murder appears as an ordinary
occurrence . . .

This rather elaborate statement has its cruder counterpart in
the sort of thing some South African whites will say if they are
asked to discuss the status of the negroes in the Dominion :
"the blacks would murder every white man in the country if
you gave them half a chance". Later in the chapter we shall
return to attitudes of this kind. In the next sections our task
will be to examine dispassionately the evidence bearing on

psychological differences between human groups. A serious difficulty is that it is much less easy to measure intellectual and moral qualities than it is to measure stature or muscular strength. We cannot go systematically through a list of psychological characteristics, and compare them for different human groups. All we can do is select from the miscellaneous information available the most significant facts, and show how they illustrate certain principles.

MENTAL ABILITY

The psychological quality that has been most measured is often called *intelligence*. The measuring is done by various systems of intelligence tests. The tests do not measure mechanical or mathematical ability, nor emotional stability, nor initiative, nor moral outlook ; but a high score can confidently be taken to imply a high degree of verbal ability even when the test itself is not verbal. In general, university teachers make high scores in intelligence tests, and so do members of the other learned professions. It has been remarked that this must be expected, since the tests were designed by professors. However, the fact that intelligence tests can give information about only one facet of the personality does not signify that they are useless. The research of which they are a result represents a valuable attempt to get an objective, quantitative expression for an important human quality. More than that, intelligence tests have been of undoubted value on a vast scale in, for example, the British and United States armies, in both of which they have been successfully used (together with other tests) in the selection of men and women for different tasks.

Intelligence tests, however, were originally designed for testing the educability of children. For this purpose it was desirable to have a system which would enable teachers and psychologists to compare children of different ages. This is what the *intelligence quotient* (IQ) does. The method is this. For a given community, such as London, a representative sample of schoolchildren of all ages from five to fourteen are given tests, and the average achievement for each age is worked out. Afterwards, any child can be tested and compared with the norm. If a child of ten scores the average mark for ten-year olds his mental age is ten ; if he scores the average for eleven-year olds his mental age is eleven (and some people might call him "precocious"). To calculate IQ :

$$IQ = \frac{\text{mental age x 100}}{\text{age in years}}$$

Thus the IQ of the ten-year child with a mental age of eleven is 110. Up to fourteen years mental age increases at a regular rate, but after that the rate of increase slows down. In England it is considered that an IQ of 120 or more is required if a child is to profit from a higher education ; and children with IQ of less than 70 are classed as dull and backward, and may be given special schooling.

Since IQ is calculated by comparing mental age with age in time, it cannot be applied to adults. A man of forty will score no higher, as a rule, than he did at twenty, although his age in time is doubled : his mental age remains unchanged, or nearly so. In this and the next two chapters, therefore, in discussing the results of these tests on different human groups, the letter I will be used to refer to scores obtained in intelligence tests by adults, irrespective of the particular set of tests used. "Intelligence", like "race", is popularly used in a variety of ways, and this is not the place for a discussion of its various meanings ; the word is therefore best avoided.

If we are to compare average I's, say of American negroes and whites, we cannot interpret the figures correctly unless we know something about the extent to which I is influenced by heredity and environment. It has been claimed, and still is sometimes claimed, that the results of intelligence tests are unaffected by environmental changes : that differences in health and education, for instance, are not reflected in the intelligence quotient. Chapter 2 gave the general, biological grounds which justify us in doubting claims of this sort, and there is now much direct evidence that I is considerably influenced, not only by genetic variation between individuals, but also by environmental differences.

In any particular child it is found that the IQ is fairly constant from year to year unless there is a drastic change in the child's environment. Mental age on the whole increases at the same rate as age in years. Illness, accident and malnutrition may affect IQ, but their influence is demonstrable only in extreme cases. Changes that have permanent effects on IQ are those which last for some years, and this applies particularly to changes that occur before the child is seven years old. Attendance at nursery school, for instance, has been shown to influence IQ, and, in general, schooling is found to have more effect than the economic or cultural background of the home. This effect of schooling is reflected in the rise in IQ that takes place in negro children in the United States when they are brought by their parents from country districts to cities. The earlier they come to town, the more nearly, on the average, do they approximate in IQ to the white children in the same schools. It has also been claimed that special schooling for a few years can greatly raise the mental age of imbecile and backward children, especially if it is begun early.

It is in the United States, with its very mixed population, that the greatest volume of work has been done on racial and national differences of I. The first fact fully established was that, in the United States, literate negroes had, on the average, lower I's than literate whites. This was clear from the results of testing army recruits in 1917. It was noticeable that recruits from the different states gave widely different averages, although within each state the negro average was always lower than the white. The differences were so great that negroes from some northern states scored higher than whites from the south. Since the southern states were, and are, backward in educational matters, this suggested that there was an environmental effect arising from variation in schooling. The lower average of negroes in each state might, it follows, be due to the fact that nearly everywhere in the United States negroes are economically and socially inferior to whites, and have correspondingly inferior facilities for their children. Other investigations have brought evidence that negroes can sometimes reach white average levels, or even surpass them. Thus in 1923 it was reported that 500 negro children tested in Los Angeles had a mean IQ of 104.7, which was a little above that of the whites.

It has been suggested that results of this sort can be accounted for by selective emigration of the more able negroes to places such as Los Angeles. The migration theory is however pure surmise, and there is no evidence for it. Comparison of the IQ's of children of parents who have emigrated has shown that, on the whole, they do not differ from those of the non-migrant children shortly after migration has taken place.

The results of testing American whites and negroes can be summarised in Klineberg's words : "The most probable interpretation," he says,

is that when American Negroes live under relatively favorable environmental conditions their test scores are correspondingly high, and when whites live under relatively poor conditions their test scores are correspondingly low. It is apparently not 'race' but environment which is the crucial variable. As for the factors in the environment which are mainly responsible . . . , it is likely that the nature of the available schooling plays a major role. A glance at the figures for per capita expenditure for Negro and white children in the segregated school system of the South brings into sharp focus the handicaps of the Negro children ; the figures also reveal that Southern white children suffer similar, though not such extreme, handicaps.

The results of comparing negroes with whites have been given at length, partly because there is a widespread belief in the inferiority of dark-skinned persons, and partly because of the abundance of evidence. These results are, moreover, quite characteristic of those obtained from any study of the correlation between physical features (such as skin colour, nose shape and so forth) with I. Investigation has, for instance, shown no correlation at all between head shape and I, or between hair colour and I. Comparison of individuals of Nordic, Alpine and Mediterranean types in Germany, France and Italy has revealed no significant differences between them, although, in each country, city dwellers (as in the United States) were found to score higher, on the average, than country folk. Once again, it seems, we have an example of the importance of environmental differences.

Even if further investigation shows that some correlation does exist between some physical character and I, we can be fairly confident that every large human group will be found to

overlap every other in the distribution of I among its members :
every group will be found to include people of both high and
low I. It follows that the results of intelligence tests are not
likely to justify social discrimination against any particular
group. The knowledge we have suggests that we can look
forward to the appearance of many men and women of intellectual ability from races and nations which at present produce
none, or very few ; what is needed is the improvement of
educational and other facilities.

CRIME

We cannot yet measure many other aspects of human behaviour
as we measure I. Some types of behaviour of social importance
are, however, reflected in the figures of conviction for various
crimes. Since it has often been held that some "races" are
particularly prone to certain types of crime it will be useful
to examine the evidence on this point.

Statistics of crime are very difficult to interpret. This is
clearly shown by the difficulties met with in the United States,
with its mixed population. Suppose, for example, that the
Irish and the Italians in America are to be compared, we can
hardly hope to learn about the criminal propensities of the
Irish and the Italians in general : the immigrants from the
two countries may constitute two quite unrepresentative
samples : it might be that, on the whole, the best types of
Italian were reaching America, and the worst types of Irish,
or vice versa. If, on the other hand, the figures for the Irish
in Ireland are compared with those for the Italians in Italy the
comparison is likely to be vitiated by differences in laws and in
enforcement in the two countries. Even in a single country
different groups may be treated differently : it is a commonplace, admitted by American sociologists, that negroes in the
United States (and especially in the south) are more likely to
be arrested for criminal offences, and, once arrested, more
likely to be convicted, than whites.

Another type of difficulty is met if the attempt is made to
compare the criminality of Jews and non-Jews. Professor
Bonger, a dutch criminologist, has published figures for the
criminality of Jews in Germany and other countries for various

years from 1882 to 1916. They show that Jews were less likely than others to commit crimes of violence, sexual crimes, theft or embezzlement. Murder and theft, in particular, were about three times as common among non-Jews. But Jews had a worse record for fraud and forgery. This might be held to support the view that Jews are "naturally" dishonest. In fact, it gives us no evidence on this question at all. A very high proportion of Jews in most countries are shopkeepers or are employed in business, and a correspondingly low proportion in manual work. Manual workers, whether in town or country, have little opportunity for fraud or forgery, and even those with criminal tendencies are therefore unlikely to commit these crimes. To get significant figures we should therefore have to compare, not Jews in general with non-Jews in general, but, say, Jewish shopkeepers with non-Jewish, and so on. If such a comparison showed marked differences it would then be necessary to see whether the differences could be ascribed to features in the family life and upbringing of the two groups, or whether there was evidence for "natural", or genetical, difference.

There is, in fact, no evidence whatever for "racial" or genetic differences in criminal tendency between large groups. On the other hand it is obvious that upbringing has a very marked effect on behaviour. What in most communities would be called murder is in some regarded as a virtuous and even necessary act : in such diverse areas as Sicily and parts of India vendetta and family feuds are, or have been, a normal element in the life of the people. What is more, the effect of upbringing in such matters can be shown very clearly not to be transmitted from generation to generation ; this is done by studying families which have migrated to a new environment. Here, for instance, are the figures for persons committed for homicide or assault in Massachusetts in 1915 :

Group	Commitments per 100,000
Born in Italy	192
American born, one or both parents born in Italy	24
American born of American parents	24
American born, one or both parents foreign but not Italian	22

These figures suggest that in large groups of people, the amount of crime is very strongly influenced by the environment, or "culture", in which they are brought up. Another example illustrates a further point. Here are the figures of convictions of first and second generation Irish immigrants in Massachusetts in 1908-9 :

Offence		Irish Immigrants	Second Generation	Native Whites
Homicide	..	2.3	1.0	0.5
Rape	..	0.0	0.3	0.7
Gaming	..	1.2	2.7	3.6

Thus a change of environment may influence not only the amount of crime, but also the nature of the crimes committed.

Some work has been done on the social factors that influence crime. Both in New York City and in London it has been found that there is a high correlation between overcrowding and child delinquency. Of course, overcrowding and poverty go together, and it may be poverty, or certain consequences of it, that are specifically responsible for increased delinquency. Klineberg, however, quotes a social experiment in which an area in Chicago with a high delinquency rate was provided with a large number of recreational facilities, such as gymnasiums, playgrounds and clubs. These measures alone brought about a rapid decrease in delinquency.

It must not be thought that this argument is intended to prove that we are all alike in our inherited capacities for crime or for virtuous behaviour. We need not doubt that there is great genetic variation in the ability, in any particular environment, to become law-abiding or the opposite. What the argument does suggest is that the differences between large human groups, in the amount of anti-social behaviour that they display, reflects primarily differences in custom ; and that these differences can be rapidly altered. As far as we know at present any group can, given the appropriate conditions, produce large numbers of crooks ; equally, given other conditions, we may suppose that any group can reach a state in which the behaviour of its members is almost uniformly lawful.

The Origins of Race Theories

Since no rational case can be made for theories of the inherited and unalterable superiority of one human group over another, it is reasonable to ask how "racism" has become so widespread. The defeat of the German fascists, the most notorious of the propagandists of race theory, has indeed put views on the superiority of a German or "aryan" race in the background. But there remain plenty of Englishmen who think that men with dark skins are their natural inferiors, and Americans who think the same of negroes and Asiatics.

This is a point where it is not possible to separate human biology from sociology and politics. Colour bars, for instance, are found where men of one physical type are ruled by aliens of another type. This is the case in the colonial empires of Britain, France and Holland. This political structure is often supported by biological assertions. A slightly different situation is found in the United States, where the blacks are in a numerical minority and are the descendants of slaves brought from Africa.

Certainly the ruling group have sometimes an obviously more advanced type of society than the ruled. The important question is whether this relationship can be regarded as permanent. In the most advanced societies of the 20th century it is taken for granted that every individual should enjoy certain rights, including a free education up to a definite age and the vote in elections for central and local governments. But it is a fact that these rights are denied to a great part of the world's population. The study of history, without any help from biology, suggests that we are not justified in thinking this situation permanent or inevitable. Colonial or semi-colonial countries such as China (until recently), India and Egypt have in the past had civilisations that were far in advance of those of Western Europe at the time. Chinese emperors have been in a position to treat white ambassadors with open contempt, and dark-skinned North Africans have written of the immature barbarians of northern Europe. The facts given earlier in this chapter confirm the plasticity of human behaviour from generation to generation, and suggest that it is possible for changes to take place very

Woman of Tierra del Fuego

MONGOLOIDS

Girl of Tierra del Fuego : this child is a pure Fuegan, yet resembles a Chinese more than she does the woman in the left-hand photograph

PLATE 9

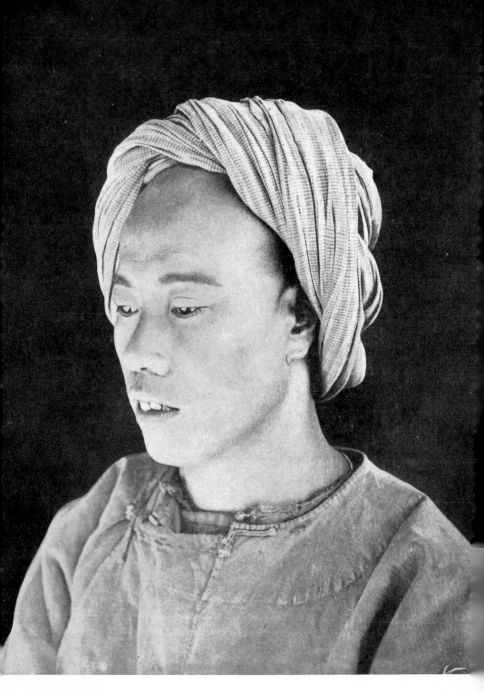

PLATE 10

MONGOLOID

Chinese coolie. (The tooth formation is not a "racial" character, but suggests malnutrition.) This, with the three preceding photographs, illustrates the variety of types within one of the major groups in which men are classified

PLATE 11

AUSTRALOIDS
Arunta girls of pure Australian aborigine stock

PLATE 12

A PRODUCT OF "RACE" CROSSING

Offspring of a white and an Australian aborigine : there is no
evidence of physical disharmony

rapidly. Thus theories of racial superiority may be regarded as reflecting the political situation in any particular historical period, but as having no biological foundation.

This is not the whole story : it does not account for race *hatred*. It is sometimes thought that dislike of one human type for another is inevitable. This is certainly untrue, since children of different types brought up together show no special antagonism. There is no doubt that race hatred exists only where it has been taught. The ease with which it can be taught is perhaps one of the most remarkable things about it. A full explanation would require a complex, psychological discussion, but one important factor is the common desire for a scapegoat. When the Germans were going through a bad time the anti-semitic doctrines of the Nazis encouraged them to put the blame for their difficulties on the Jews. Most people have aggressive tendencies more or less kept in check ; some give them an outlet by playing strenuous games or by watching films about gangsters. However, it is convenient to have some class of people, marked off fairly sharply from one's own group, towards whom one can direct this aggressiveness without offending the neighbours. This fact has been exploited by the fascists in Britain : in the East End of London they try to generate anti-Semitism ; in Cardiff they attack the negro community ; in Liverpool the immigrant Irish are the target.

These psychological tendencies are in fact encouraged by all who profit from racial and national divisions. In many parts of the world today dark-skinned people form an important source of cheap labour for farmers and industrialists. If their wages and conditions of work were improved profits might fall, or disappear. Thus in one gold-mining district of South Africa in 1937 the 36,000 European workers had an average annual income of £390, while the 280,000 non-Europeans received £47. If all types of workers combined in trade unions, as has happened in some parts of the United States, the inferior position of the non-Europeans would no doubt rapidly improve, to the disadvantage of their employers. Thus in South Africa, as in many other countries, it is to the advantage of the ruling and employing group to maintain "racial" divisions, and to support them with lies about human biology.

THE JEWS

The so-called "Jewish problem" resembles the problems touched on in the last section in having political, economic, psychological and religious aspects ; some of them have already been mentioned. Anti-semitism is so profoundly irrational that it can hardly be made the subject of a straight-forward, biological discussion ; or at least, if it were, the argument would have no effect on anti-semites, and would be superfluous for anyone else. However, the biological facts about Jews are not well known, and are worth summarising. Huxley & Haddon say :

> The Jews can rank neither as nation nor even as ethnic unit, but rather as a socio-religious group carrying large Mediterranean, Armenoid and many other elements, and varying greatly in physical characters. Like many other groups its members are held together partly by external pressure of various kinds, partly by a long historic memory, partly by a sense of common suffering, partly by a religion.

During the Roman Empire there was a great increase in the number of Jews, as a result of the conversion of people of many different types in many countries to Judaism. Physically the Jews today are very variable, and in each country they tend to resemble the non-Jewish natives. This is due to mixed marriages with non-Jews, and is most apparent in Jewish communities which have been established for many centuries. Chinese Jews are Chinese in appearance, Abyssinian Jews resemble other Abyssinians. The so-called Jewish nose resembles that often found in persons of the Armenoid type, and is not by any means universal among Jews nor confined to them. In parts of Poland, and in Alsace, a high proportion of Jews are blonds, although typically Jews (like most people) are dark. There is no uniformity in head shape or in stature. Many people claim to be able to identify Jews by their appearance, but when their claims are tested on large numbers of people they make many mistakes : they often fail to identify Jews as such, and they may identify as Jews people, for instance Armenians, who are not Jewish at all.

As for statements about the Jewish character, they have been sufficiently dealt with already. We can summarise by saying that, not only are the Jews not a race in any sense of the word, but their behaviour, social or anti-social, is just as much a product of the conditions in which they live as is that of any other group.

MIXED BREEDING

Another question which arouses much emotion is that of the desirability of marriage between persons of widely different physical type. Where racism and colour bars exist such inter-marriage is certain to be regarded as a grave social crime, and in some countries it is illegal. There have been instances in British colonies of white women receiving terms of imprisonment for cohabiting with natives. Even where the law does not intervene convention will often make intermarriage difficult and dangerous.

The question for us is whether there are biological objections to intermarriage. It is sometimes believed that there are, because the children of such marriages are in some countries often very unsatisfactory. This, however, is a *non sequitur*. Where there is a colour bar it is often the poorest people of the two colours who intermarry, and poverty alone (as we shall see in the next and later chapters) is a severe handicap. More-over half-breeds may be despised by both elements, and so suffer psychological disadvantages as well.

Intermarriage does not necessarily produce either biological or social difficulties. In New Zealand there has been success-ful intermarriage between Maoris and whites : there is little colour feeling, and a Maori has been acting Prime Minister. In such diverse regions as Hawaii and South America "race crossing" has been and is practised without ill effects. If the whole of history is examined it is found that "race mixture" has been frequent, and it is impossible to show that it has had undesirable results.

Attempts have been made to show that marriage between certain types, such as negroes and English in Liverpool, pro-duces children in whom the different parts of the skeleton do not conform : in whom, for instance, the teeth of the upper and lower jaws fail to fit together in a normal manner. The results so far used to support this view have however not taken account of the effects of malnutrition, and are therefore unconvincing. In crosses between widely different breeds of animals, such as dogs, no such failure to conform is found, and it would be surprising if it were discovered in man.

In general, it can be confidently said that "race crossing" is a social, not a biological problem. Biologically, the marriage of very diverse types serves to increase the variability of man, and to produce a larger number of genetic combinations than had previously existed. From this point of view it is desirable, since it increases the possibility of genetic combinations of especial value to society.

CHAPTER 8

THE INEQUALITY OF MAN

DESPITE the magnificent prose and admirable intentions of the American Declaration of Independence, it is not true that all men are created equal. All Cox's orange pippin trees are "created equal" in the sense of having the same genes, because all are derived by vegetative propagation from one original tree. But man, like most animal and plant species, reproduces sexually ; his genes are consequently, as we have seen, re-combined in new groups at each fertilisation, and, apart from uniovular twins, each individual is genetically unique. We know that there is no good evidence for innate psychological differences between races. Despite this, there is certainly much genetical variation *within* each human group. The subject of innate inequality has become peculiarly confused with the political question of equality of opportunity. The Declaration of Independence is primarily concerned to assert the right of every person to life, liberty and the pursuit of happiness ; but this holds irrespective of innate differences between individuals. The main source of the confusion has been the attempt by some to claim especial virtues for particular classes : just as some "races" have been said to be superior to the rest, so genetic superiority has been claimed for the middle or upper classes within a single nation.

EUGENICS

This sort of claim has been especially associated with eugenic propaganda. The founder of the eugenic movement was an Englishman, Francis Galton. Galton was a brilliant mathematician ; he was a pioneer of the use of statistical methods in biology ; he invented the finger-print method of identification ; and he interested himself in a wide variety of research problems, including some unconventional ones such as the statistical investigation of the efficacy of prayer. He was the first President of the Eugenics Education Society (now the Eugenics Society), which was founded in London in 1908.

Some of the early pronouncements of leading members of this society, including scientists, were of such a character as to bring the ideas of eugenics into disrepute. A distinguished mathematician remarked, for example, that the upper classes contained all the finest examples of beauty, goodness and taste. It was asserted that the poor were genetically less fit than the wealthy, and on these grounds old age pensions (5/– a week at the age of seventy), and free meals in schools, were opposed, since such measures were held to encourage the improvident poor to breed more and so to produce an excess of inferior types. Attention was drawn to the fact that, at that time, the more wealthy families produced fewer children than poorer ones. It has been said that the eugenics movement was a passionate protest against the fact that the meek do inherit the earth.

Eugenic propaganda now rarely takes these forms. The importance of environmental agencies, such as nutrition and housing, has (as we shall see in chapters 12 and 13) become so clear that poor physical development is no longer attributed to "bad inheritance" ; and mass unemployment has made it difficult to regard poverty as an inherited character. It is therefore easier to consider the question of eugenics in a matter-of-fact way, and to enquire to what extent our knowledge of human genetics could be used for eugenic purposes.

There is, in principle, nothing absurd in the idea of the planned breeding of human beings. The selective breeding of domestic animals is such a well established practice that it was inevitable that men should think of applying similar methods to themselves. Such speculation did not await the development of human genetics : the subject was discussed in the ancient world. In the fifth book of Plato's *Republic* we find the following passage :

> And those of the youth who have distinguished themselves, whether in war or anywhere else, ought to have awards and prizes given them, and the most ample liberty of embracing women, so that under this pretext likewise the greatest number of children may be generated of such persons.

However, neither the Greeks nor any other large human group have yet tried to put the principle of selective mating into practice. (The Germans under the Nazis were perhaps an exception.) There are primitive peoples among whom children thought to be defective or superfluous are killed ; but although this practice may have a favourable effect on the populations concerned it is not advocated by modern eugenists.

Most eugenic programmes aim at preventing the breeding of the "unfit". This is *negative eugenics*, by contrast with positive eugenics aimed at promoting the breeding of the especially gifted. The means of preventing reproduction include propaganda and contraceptives ; the segregation of persons in institutions ; and sterilisation, either optional or compulsory. Among other countries Denmark, Norway and Sweden have sterilisation laws, and some States of the U.S.A. In Nazi Germany a sterilisation law giving very wide powers was passed in 1934. Legislation has been proposed for the United Kingdom, but has not been before Parliament.

What can sterilisation do ? This depends on the precise way in which defects are influenced by the genes. Some diseases can be said without qualification to be inherited, because environment plays no significant part in their advent. Of these, a few are due to dominant genes. Thus the condition of brachydactyly, or short fingers, due to a failure of normal growth in the middle bone, is passed on by an affected person to half his or her children, on the average. The condition is transmitted only by affected persons. Brachydactyly is itself a not very severe defect, and does not prevent a useful and normal life. On the other hand, lobster claw, or split hand, which is inherited in the same way, is a severe handicap. There are a least sixteen other defects known to be transmitted in the same way, but some of them are relatively slight. Moreover, they may vary in severity : for instance, lamellar cataract may consist of a large opaque body involving most of the lens and causing nearly complete blindness, or a very small defect compatible with excellent sight.

It is clear that sterilisation of all persons with lobster claw could be expected to bring about a rapid reduction in the number of people with that defect. Since the gene responsible takes effect in every individual who carries it, all these individuals can be identified. However, the total amount of serious defect due to genes of this type is very small in any large population, and the eugenic effect of sterilising affected persons, or of otherwise preventing their breeding, would be trivial.

GENERATION

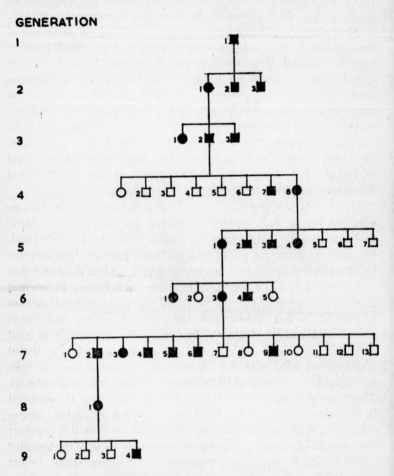

PART OF A PEDIGREE SHOWING TRANSMISSION OF A DOMINANT
CHARACTER

Pedigree of "congenital" stationary night-blindness, a defect due to a dominant gene. Note that it appears regularly in each generation ; it is transmitted only by affected persons (of either sex), but not to all their offspring

Some other diseases are due to recessive genes. With these it is unusual for affected individuals to have affected parents. Just as a red-haired person may have parents both with non-red hair, so a child with, for example, "congenital" deaf-mutism may have normal parents : each parent has passed on one gene responsible for the complaint. Sterilisation of all persons suffering from congenital deaf-mutism would do little to reduce the incidence of the condition : according to Haldane "there would be no noticeable effect in less than thirty or forty generations". Normal persons carrying the gene would continue to produce deaf mutes as before.

There are some genetically determined diseases of such severity that affected persons hardly ever survive to produce offspring. In other words, with these diseases the aspiring eugenist is forestalled by "natural causes". But if all affected persons are prevented from leaving offspring, how is it that the genes concerned persist in the population, and continue to produce deficient individuals ?

An example is hæmophilia. As we saw in chapter 3 hæmophilia is due to a recessive sex-linked gene : it is known only in males, who derive the gene from their mothers, and who rarely survive to have children. The repeated appearance of hæmophilics in a population is due to mutation : the gene responsible for hæmophilia is an inexact copy of a normal gene ; and it has been calculated that this normal gene mutates at the rate of one in fifty thousand. This is probably an unusually high mutation rate.

It is clear that deficiencies maintained in a population by recurrent mutation cannot be seriously affected by eugenic measures.

So far we have considered only diseases determined in a relatively simple way. But advocates of negative eugenics have commonly been more concerned with conditions, such as mental deficiency, which are far from simple. It is sometimes claimed that the level of intelligence of whole populations is threatened by the excessive breeding of mental defectives. If "mental deficiency" were a simply defined condition, like albinism, and transmitted in a straightforward way from parent to offspring, it might be possible to make a rational plan to reduce its incidence. But the opposite is true. The children who attend special schools for mental deficiency include a great variety of types, each owing the deficiency to a different set of causes. Some types are curable, for instance by psychotherapy. At least five, and perhaps as many as twenty per cent can, by the application of existing knowledge, be so improved as to become useful and normal citizens. As for the genetics of mental deficiency, out of every hundred children with one or both parents defective, about seven or eight are themselves found to be mentally deficient. A larger proportion are found to be backward, but the majority are normal. Just as mentally defective parents can have normal children, so can normal parents have mentally defective children. Indeed, most defective children have normal parents.

It follows that eugenic measures can do little to prevent the appearance of mental defectives ; and that, if all defectives were sterilised or otherwise prevented from breeding, this would prevent the production of many more normal children than of defectives.

WASTED ABILITIES

Even if negative eugenics would be of little use with our present knowledge, it might still be true that there are important genetic differences between classes. We have seen in the previous chapter that no such differences can be demonstrated between races or nations, but it does not follow that they are not to be found between, say, the professional and managerial group on the one hand, and the unskilled labourers on the other. This is a difficult question to investigate, because in most countries the conditions in which the children of these two classes grow up are exceedingly different. The influence of environment both on physique and on mental abilities has been repeatedly mentioned already. In chapters 12 and 13 more detailed accounts will be found of differences in nutrition and in exposure to infection. There is no doubt that these influences have an important effect on height, weight, strength and length of life, but whether there are also genetical differences is not known.

If we wish to consider psychological differences we are

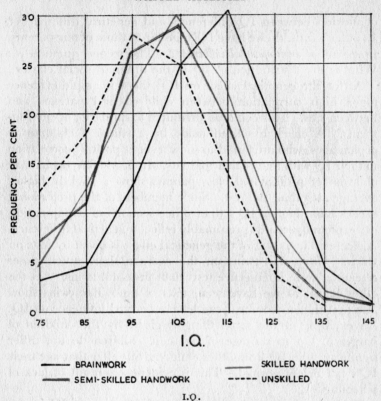

I.Q.

Distribution of intelligence quotient among the children of members of different economic classes. The wealthier children score better, on the average, than the poor, but there is a big overlap. We do not know to what extent the class difference is due to environment.

Distribution curves are described on pages 36 and 37

compelled, as in the previous chapter, to fall back on measurements of intelligence quotients, with all their limitations already described. However, although they do not give us information about many valuable qualities, varying from mechanical ability to emotional stability, and although IQ is influenced by environment, intelligence tests nevertheless give us some valuable information about the distribution of ability within a nation.

There are two questions to ask here. First, is there any

connexion between IQ differences and genetical differences ? In other words, do we have IQ's similar to those of our parents, *irrespective of environmental influences* ? The second question is : What is the distribution of IQ in the different social classes ?

As for the genetical effect on IQ, there is ample evidence for a high correlation between children and parents, and between sibs. This could be attributed to similarity of environments. A check has been made by a study of children in orphanages, who are found to show a slight positive correlation in their IQ with that of their parents. In particular, orphanage children of professional class parents show a slightly higher average IQ than the rest. Since members of the professional classes have higher IQ's than other sections of a population the orphanage results presumably reflect a genetical difference. A clearer illustration of the genetical effect is given by tests on twins. Uniovular twins on the average show much closer resemblance in intelligence tests than fraternal twins. On the other hand, as we have seen, tests of uniovular twins show also that the environment can have a marked influence on IQ. An example of the same thing is given by the children of bargees. Up to the age of six these children do not differ significantly in IQ from other children, but after that age their IQ's fall below normal. This is evidently a result of lack of schooling.

The second question, that of the distribution of IQ in the social classes, is partly answered in the figure on page 127. It will be seen at once that in England the highest income group has the highest average IQ, and the highest proportion of very gifted individuals. On the other hand there is a big overlap : even the lowest group has a considerable number of individuals with high IQ's. In fact, since the lower income groups form the great majority of the population, they include more individuals of exceptionally high IQ than the higher groups.

We cannot say to what extent the difference between the classes is genetically determined. We have already seen that some, at least, is probably due to the inferior amenities of the poor. The immediate conclusion to be drawn, for practical purposes, is that there is no sharp distinction in IQ scores between the different classes : all classes have individuals with

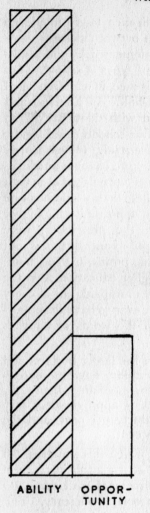
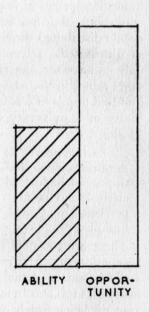

ABILITY AND OPPORTUNITY FOR SCHOOL-CHILDREN IN ENGLAND AND
WALES BEFORE 1940

The majority, from poor families, went to free schools, and only a
small proportion of the able ones had the opportunity for further
education. Among the children of wealthy parents, attending
expensive schools, there was more opportunity than ability

both high and low scores, and intelligence tests provide no grounds for educational discrimination between classes.

These facts and figures can be supplemented by the results of taking the IQ's of pupils in different types of school. Let us consider the distribution of intelligence in children aged between nine years and twelve-and-a-half. In England and Wales, out of every hundred children with quotients of 120 and over, about 84 are found in the free schools (used by the poor) and 16 in those in which fees are paid. (These figures apply to the period before 1939 but, despite changes in educational administration, there still remains a privileged class with better opportunities than the rest.) These facts would be of no immediate practical importance if the opportunity for higher education, and for advancement in the professions, were evenly distributed throughout the population. But it is not so distributed. Of every hundred able pupils in free schools only 36 have the opportunity for a higher education ; on the other hand, in the schools in which fees are paid, out of every hundred pupils *without* high ability just over 50 have the opportunity of a university education. In the words of Gray & Moshinsky :

. . . while nearly all the children of the larger business and the professional classes who possess ability have the opportunity of higher education, the corresponding figure for clerical and commercial employees is approximately fifty per cent, for skilled wage-earners thirty per cent, and the unskilled wage-earners twenty per cent.

There are two points of view from which this situation can be considered. Many will regard it as a glaring instance of social injustice. It indicates no disagreement with that view to say that it is also an instance of gross social inefficiency. This aspect is being widely emphasised as this book is written. The problems of a post-war period have found most countries with far fewer trained scientists and technicians than they need. In Britain a government White Paper has urged a rapid doubling of the number of students in the universities. The same report points out that there is a large untapped reserve of ability among the children of the poor. This view has been reinforced by investigations in which the I of university students has been compared with that of the general population. In England rather less than two per cent of the population reach the universities. If we take the half of these with the higher I's we find that their I is 124 or more. This group, being only half the university population, amounts to about one per cent of the total population. The next question is : what proportion of the total population have I's similar to those of the best half of the university students ? The answer is that, at student ages, 5.3 per cent have I's of 124 or more. It follows that only about one in five of those whose I is within the range of that of the best half of the students ever reaches a university. Of course, I does not test all the qualities needed in a university student. No doubt some of those with high I's would be quite unsuited to a university education. This indeed applies to those who are already students as well as to the less fortunate. But when all allowances are made it is still clear that university education is far from open to all those who could profit from it.

This emphasis on the reserve of ability to be found among the poor and unprivileged may seem to conflict with a widely propagated theory that the "national intelligence" of Britain is declining. The theory is based on the following argument : the rich (that is, the professional and managerial class) have children whose average IQ is higher than that of the children of the poor ; but the poor on the average have larger families than the rich ; the difference in IQ between rich and poor is, at least in part, genetically determined ; therefore the proportion of those with high mental ability is steadily being reduced. This view has been criticised on various grounds. For instance, as we shall see further in chapter 14, the differential fertility between rich and poor may be only a temporary phenomenon. More important, it has been suggested that the difference in IQ between rich and poor children may be a product of the inferior conditions, both physical and mental, of the poor. The theory has now however been directly tested. In 1932 87,000 Scottish children aged eleven years did intelligence tests ; in 1947 nearly 71,000 eleven-year-olds did similar tests. Out of a maximum score of 76 points the average in 1932 was 34.5 ; in 1947 it was 36.7. This difference can be shown not to be due to chance, and it follows that the IQ of Scottish children has risen during the period of fifteen years covered by the experiment. We do not know what has caused the rise : it may be improved environment, especially nutrition. It is however permissible to conclude that alarm about declining intelligence is premature.

It is not possible to give figures for other countries comparable with those which have been worked out for England, but the variety of conditions elsewhere can be illustrated by considering three other great powers. First we may take China, where a majority of the population is illiterate : only a very few have any formal education at all. Despite this, a few small, ill-equipped universities have shown that there is no lack of talent. This state of affairs holds for much more than half the world's population.

The second country is the U.S.A. In the United States as many as 15 per cent of the population receive some kind of university education. Most of this 15 per cent are drawn from the upper income group, referred to above as "professional and managerial", and about 90 per cent of the children of this group go to college. The middle income group send only fifteen per cent of their children to college, and the third group, of the lower paid workers, send only five per cent. Yet the great majority of American children (about 60 per cent) belong to this last group. A Harvard University committee considers that about 125,000 American children each year could profit from going to college, and would go if they could, but are prevented by poverty. More recently the President's Committee on Higher Education has reported that, on the basis of ability alone, there are two or three times as many potential university students as actually reach a university. The Harvard committee assert further that

> if . . . the social environment of these young people should improve materially, more of them would almost certainly show higher promise. There is experimental evidence that ability can be improved as a child's early surroundings are improved—evidence which, as was said, the growth and spread of talent which have accompanied the decline of privilege in the modern era tends to confirm.

Finally, in the U.S.S.R. there is a system of free, compulsory education for all children ; all schools have the same status, and there is no section of the population whose children attend university by virtue of their parents' wealth. The soviet system is still undergoing rapid change and development, and it is not yet complete ; when this phase is over it may give valuable information on ways of avoiding the waste of talent that undoubtedly occurs elsewhere.

ABILITY AND SOCIAL USEFULNESS

The conclusion we reach, then, from the study of psychological differences between classes, is the same as that on race differences : that there is no sound evidence for average genetical differences between groups. This is true, even though the individuals within any one group differ very greatly from each other. It may be expected that any large human group, whether it is defined geographically, or by physical features, or by economic status, will produce a proportion of persons of high ability, and also some of low ability. It is perfectly possible that some groups differ in average innate ability from others, but there is no reason to think that, if they do exist, the differences are great enough to justify reserving educational privileges, or entry into certain professions, for members of a particular class.

We have so far ignored the fact that human society requires many widely different types for its smooth running. Professor Spearman has said that every individual is a genius at something, as well as an idiot at something ; and he added that it remains to discover what—at any rate in respect of the genius. This statement may seem a little extreme. But it is safe to say that most individuals could find something useful and pleasant to do among the available occupations. (Even mentally deficient persons, it is said, make excellent pig-minders, since they are content with highly monotonous tasks.) To put the point in a more general form : if we wish to assess the worth of an individual we must specify very precisely the mode of life the individual is to adopt.

To sum up, it seems that every race, and each economic class within a nation, can produce its quota of the good and bad, intelligent and stupid, strong and weak. This is just as well.

The view is becoming more and more widely held that every human being is entitled to certain essentials of civilised life, including food, clothes and shelter, together with a certain amount of leisure in which to enjoy them in his own way. If this principle had to be applied to large populations incapable of making an adequate contribution to world prosperity, the outlook would be depressing : the more advanced peoples would have to accept for many decades a much lowered standard of life, while a large fraction of the products of their labour went to the less fortunate and the less capable. The actual outlook is quite different. There is every reason to think that, once depressed races and classes are set on the road of social development, they will soon make a contribution to the material and intellectual wealth of mankind commensurate with their numbers.

CHAPTER 9

SEX DIFFERENCES

> Social progress can be measured with precision by the social position of the female sex.
>
> KARL MARX

THE most obvious aspect of human variety, the differentiation into two sexes, remains to be discussed. Unfortunately the amount of precise knowledge of sex differences, apart from the obvious anatomical and physiological ones, is surprisingly small, while misunderstanding and prejudice are correspondingly great. Dogmatic but quite unsupported views are widely held on what is typical and unalterable in the characters, temperaments and abilities of the two sexes.

In most societies the different social positions of men and women are based directly on their different rôles in reproduction : women bear children and suckle them, and so are tied to the home and to household duties ; men are not so tied, and must undertake the outside tasks : hunting in a primitive community, tilling the fields in a peasant community, and carrying on the various trades and professions in a modern society. It is natural to take this situation for granted, and to believe that women are not fitted for the tasks normally carried out by men. Thus a century ago there were no women doctors, and many took it for granted that women had not the capacity to become doctors. Many such assumptions are based on nothing more than local custom : in the third century A.D. the Greek, Athenæus, exclaimed, "Whoever heard of a woman cook ! "

In this chapter we shall not be concerned with the main physical differences between the sexes : these can be studied in textbooks of anatomy and physiology. We shall deal with the secondary differences—those arising only indirectly from the different reproductive functions of men and women. Once again we shall have to try to sort out the effects of heredity and environment. Owing to its social implications this question has become, like that of race and of eugenics, partly a political one. It has been asserted that conventional views on the abilities of women are determined, not by the true facts, but by prejudice associated with their depressed position in a society run by men. It has been claimed that there is no evidence that women are less well endowed, either physically or mentally, than men, and that given the opportunity the two sexes could compete on equal terms in every field of human endeavour.

In the rest of this chapter we shall try to summarise what accurate information exists on this subject.

PHYSICAL DIFFERENCES

From before birth there are sex differences in growth rates and in the development of various organs. Boys, on the average, are slightly heavier than girls at birth ; on the other hand, girls show a more advanced development of the skeleton. There is no possibility of these differences being determined environmentally. As for the adult skeleton, it is usually possible for an anatomist to determine the sex even of a quite small part, such as a fragment of the skull. About one skeleton in 40 may prove difficult to place. These differences may be influenced by the different conditions in which the sexes are brought up, but it is reasonably certain that they are mainly due to genetic differences.

Boys are not only slightly heavier, on the average, at birth, but also (among Europeans) about one-third of an inch taller. This superiority of height does not persist : by eleven years the average heights of the sexes are about equal, and at thirteen girls are about three-quarters of an inch taller. But girls slow down and stop growth earlier than boys. By eighteen most have stopped, whereas boys are on the average nearly three inches ahead and still growing. (There are many individual exceptions to these generalities.) We can be certain that all this reflects genetic differences in growth capacity, even though environmental agencies may play some part. In some societies the growth of most women is checked prematurely by early child-bearing, and the difference of stature between the sexes is therefore increased. It is possible that there are less obvious environmental effects operating even among the children of the western world today. (Some may act in the opposite direction. In Italy, for instance, boys are more prized than girls, and better looked after, and as infants they are therefore kept more carefully in the shade ; but the action of sunlight on the skin produces vitamin D, and in times of food shortage, as in the period after the second world war, this may be important. Doctors doing relief work certainly found a higher relative incidence of rickets (which is caused partly by vitamin D deficiency) among boys. Whatever moral one draws from this, it is an example of an environmental effect influencing the two sexes differently.)

Males are not only bigger than females ; they also have a higher metabolic rate on the average : that is, chemical changes in their bodies go on more rapidly, and so males on the whole require more food.

Muscular strength parallels growth changes. In one study of 87 girls and 89 boys, in California, grip, pulling and thrusting strength were measured regularly throughout school and college life. Sex differences were found to be small up to the age of 13 ; after this the rate of change became much less in girls, but greater in boys. As a result, after 16 almost no girls reached even the average performance of boys, and nearly all the boys were above the girls' average. It is hardly possible to attribute this difference to environment, especially since all the children studied had plenty of opportunity for developing muscular strength through games, and nutritionally they were all in much the same state.

Muscular *skills*, on the other hand, seem to be distributed between the sexes in a more complicated way. It is a commonplace that as a rule boys throw better than girls. This might often be because they are encouraged to play more ball games. It seems, however, that there is a more fundamental difference involved. The form of the limbs, and in particular of the bones of the arm, is different in the two sexes : so girls, for anatomical reasons, may be obliged to throw in a less effective way than boys. And it is reasonably certain that the anatomical differences are determined genetically. But throwing is, perhaps, not of much importance. In some other types of skilled activity girls do better than boys from a very early age. Anything requiring the performance of delicate movements is found to be done better by girls : for instance, they learn to dress earlier, on the whole. It has been claimed that differences in the capacity to carry out fine movements can be observed as early as nine months.

So far, then, there is some objective basis for referring to women as "the weaker sex" : they are measurably less strong than men, on the average (though not less skilled), and the difference is probably mainly a genetical one. But in another respect it is men who are the weaker sex. They die more easily. This is largely due to a lower resistance to infection which holds throughout life. The possible genetical basis of this difference has been described in chapter 3. It does not, however, apply in all countries : in India and China, where women suffer conditions especially bad for health, the death-rate of women is higher than that of men at most ages.

Intellectual Differences

It might be expected that, on coming to psychological differences, the first step would be to compare the average IQ's of the two sexes. This, however, can be done in a sentence : the IQ's are identical. Unfortunately this tells us nothing about the relative intellectual abilities of the sexes : the fact is, the best modern intelligence tests are *designed* in such a way that boys and girls of equal age show the same average performance. However, if individual tests are studied, among the series from which IQ is calculated, it is found that boys and girls by no means do equally well in each. If we summarise the main points of difference shown in all kinds of tests, we find that boys show better mechanical ability and are more likely to excel in mathematics ; on the other hand girls from a very early age are more articulate ; they talk more, and more intelligibly. They are also superior in "æsthetic sense" : for instance, they discriminate colours better than boys. Their memory too is said to be better, at least in early childhood. Later, they are better at languages. A general difference is that boys are more variable than girls : there are more extreme types among males, for instance more with a very high IQ and more imbeciles.

An important question is whether intellectual development shows any parallel with the growth changes and physiological modifications during adolescence. It has been said that, just as girls stop growing earlier, so their "intelligence" reaches its maximum before that of boys. (To show this it is of course necessary to use tests other than those that have been standardised to show no difference between the sexes.) Whether there is any basis for this view or not, it is certain that there is a great overlap of intellectual ability between men and women. There are no grounds for denying women a higher education in any subject.

Although the psychological differences just described are quite likely to be due mainly to genetical differences, we are entirely justified in remaining sceptical on that point. It is extraordinarily difficult to discern the more subtle environmental influences, and to distinguish their effects from genetical ones. In most societies girls and boys are treated differently almost from birth : they are dressed differently, talked to differently, and *expected* to show different interests. We cannot say to what extent this attitude has prevented the appearance of eminent women in the arts and professions. The difficulty in allowing for the effects of social convention is probably greatest if we try to deal with differences of "character" or "temperament". Child psychologists and others commonly assert that, for instance, boys are more aggressive than girls, and girls shyer. We need not doubt that this is true, but unfortunately it is not easy to measure aggression or shyness, and so it is difficult to make statements of this kind quantitative and precise. It would be very rash to claim that a difference of this sort is quite independent of the social environment of the child. In any case all these statements concern the averages shown by groups : they tell us nothing about particular persons. When Samuel Johnson was asked, "Which have the most brains, men or women ? " he replied, "Which man, which woman ? " His reply could not have been more to the point.

WOMEN IN THE COMMUNITY

A possible way of assessing the environmental effects on behaviour differences between the sexes is to study different types of society. In chapter 7 we saw that racial or national groups show great plasticity of behaviour in response to different environments. Do the two sexes show a similar plasticity?

It is immediately obvious that in some respects they do. The behaviour of a well-to-do business man in Western Europe or the United States during the late nineteenth century might be contrasted with that of the dandy of less than a century before. Similarly we may make the obvious comparison of the Victorian lady dressed, perhaps, in ankle-length skirt and bustle, and the mid-twentieth century young woman in slacks and sweater.

This type of comparison, however, though interesting, is superficial, and does not take us very far. Much greater claims have been made for the alterability of the behaviour of men and women—and particularly women—than are justified by the changes that have taken place in the past few centuries in the western world. In 1879, for instance, John Stuart Mill wrote that

> What is now called the nature of women is an eminently artificial thing, the result of forced repression in some directions, unnatural stimulation in others. It may be asserted, without scruple, that no other class of dependents have had their character so entirely distorted from its natural proportions.

It is, of course, quite reasonable to suggest that the character of men, too, in 1879, as today, was in some sense "distorted from its natural proportions". Mill's emphasis on women was a protest against their position as dependents. The buying and selling of wives still occurred in England in the first half of the nineteenth century.

The protest against the subjection of women, and the demand for their emancipation from all the social and economic disadvantages imposed on them, has been supported by pointing to societies in which the rôles of the sexes have been apparently the reverse of those familiar to us. Thus in our society women are expected (on the whole) to play a passive part in love-making ; to be dependent rather than self-reliant ; to be modest, chaste, home-loving and motherly ; and to be particularly interested in self-adornment. It is claimed, however, that in some civilisations, notably those of Sparta and ancient Egypt, these characteristics have belonged on the whole to men, and not to women ; and that this reversal was related to the economic subjection of men which was characteristic of these societies.

The extent to which this account of these ancient societies is accurate has been questioned, and we cannot confidently assert from the evidence they provide that a complete inversion of behaviour is possible. On the other hand in some primitive societies today such inversion has been directly observed and studied. The most remarkable work of this kind was done by Margaret Mead in New Guinea. Of three tribal groups in that country, one, the Tchambuli, shows a relationship between the sexes the exact opposite of what we accept as usual. In both the others, however, there is "no idea that men and women are different in temperament". Of these two, in the Arapesh the behaviour of both men and women is uniformly gentle and unaggressive, and what we should describe as maternal and passive ; this group practises agriculture. On the other hand the Mundugumor, who are head-hunters, are, men and women alike, aggressive and "masculine". It is however easy to attach too much importance to these observations. After all, inversions are rare. If they can occur, we may ask, is it not significant that there are very few instances ?

Apart from primitive societies we have, in the Soviet Union, a country in which the social and legal attitude towards women differs greatly from those of most other nations. The Soviet constitution states :

Women in the U.S.S.R. are accorded equal rights with men, in all spheres of economic, state, cultural, social, and political life.

One result of this was that, by 1939, women doctors in the Soviet Union slightly outnumbered men ; another has been the much commented on women engine-drivers and ships' captains.

On the other hand the following statement appeared in a report on "Soviet Women and Defence" :

> Not all jobs were open to Soviet women, however. The Soviets saw nothing incompatible between the doctrine of equality of the sexes and the doctrine of protection of women from influences that would impair their ability to bear healthy children.

In particular, women in the Soviet Union are not considered fitted for the heaviest types of physical labour.

Conclusions of this kind have been reached, in the U.S.S.R., not on the basis of preconceptions about the abilities of the two sexes, nor on political grounds, but empirically : the experiences of the rapidly changing Soviet state have been responsible for sudden modifications of outlook and policy. In the early stages, immediately after the revolution, the emphasis was on equality, as a revolt against the degrading role allotted to women in Csarist Russia. Since the second world war, and now that the equal rights of women and men have come to be taken for granted, emphasis has been laid on the importance, both to the individual and to society, of motherhood, and special measures have been taken to make the task of bringing up children attractive and free from financial difficulties.

The distinctive feature of Soviet policy is not that it is based on special knowledge or on one consistent and unvarying plan, but that it is conscious and deliberate. If one thing (such as co-education) is considered, on the basis of experience, not to work, something else is tried. At present it is not possible to draw final conclusions from Soviet experience, any more than it is from the studies, mentioned above, carried out by physiologists or anthropologists in other countries. Just as we have yet to determine the innate abilities of different races, so we are very far from knowing what members of either sex could do, in more satisfactory environments than those so far achieved.

Part Three

LIFE AND DEATH

THE first human societies were small family groups, and only when agriculture was invented, perhaps seven thousand years ago, did populous human communities come into being. Gradual improvement in the techniques of cultivation made it possible to produce a food surplus, which could support those who grew no food but worked in industry or trade, or administered the state ; this was the foundation of civilisation. But food supplies have never been entirely reliable for any large human population. Today we can not only see the world's food problem as a whole, but also discern the biological and economic changes required to solve it.

The other major biological problem of the twentieth century is the conquest of infectious disease. Much of the world still suffers from the same epidemic and endemic scourges as our ancestors of centuries ago, although it is known how to prevent them. In the advanced countries, where they have been prevented, there remain formidable problems such as high infant mortality and tuberculosis, but these too can be solved.

If full use is to be made of biological knowledge for human benefit human populations must attain relative stability : at present most are increasing, and so are exacerbating the food problem.

CHAPTER 10

MAN AND SOCIETY

Thou shalt eat the herb of the field ; in the
sweat of thy face shalt thou eat bread . . .

GENESIS

THIS chapter is a connecting link between the fifth, on the evolution of man, and the four which follow on food, disease and population respectively. It deals with the evolution of human society. In chapter 5 man was described biologically, and his relationship with other mammals, especially the apes, was emphasised. But man is distinguished by a unique form of social organisation. It is unique because other highly social animals, such as ants and bees, have the patterns of their behaviour fixed independently of experience, whereas one of the most notable things about man, compared with other animals, is his capacity for learning, especially in his early years, and the consequent plasticity of his behaviour. The single species, *Homo sapiens*, has therefore been able to produce many different types of society ; and in some areas (such as Western Europe, or Central Asia) society has changed from one type to another very rapidly.

There is a notion that some types of human existence are more natural than others, though what *natural* means in this context is rarely explained. The "state of nature" in which primitive man exists is sometimes contrasted with the "artificiality" of modern times. The implication is that primitive men live like most other animals, without social organisation, tools or speech. But this is not true. Even before *Homo sapiens* appeared there were all these things, together with fire : wherever and whenever he has lived man has assembled in groups and has altered his surroundings so as to satisfy his needs. This is what is meant when it is said that man "creates his own environment".

Social organisation developed from family groups. Among apes today the group consists typically of a single dominant male with a number of females and their young. There is no division of labour between the sexes and all have to forage for food. In primitive man monogamy is typical. The women contribute to food-getting by gathering food plants and the men hunt. The division of labour between the sexes also makes possible greater protection for the young by the mother ; and this is essential, since in man social behaviour depends on the young gradually learning appropriate habits and customs.

SAVAGERY

This early type of society is technically called savagery, though not in any pejorative sense. It refers to the state of all pre-*sapiens* man ; and *Homo sapiens* himself has lived for 90 per cent or more of his time in the same state.

Savage man is usually nomadic. The present tense can be used here, not merely as a literary device but because there are several groups which have never progressed from savagery : for example, the Australian aborigines, the Eskimos and some of the inhabitants of Malaya and of Central and South Africa. He lives by collecting food, plant or animal, over a wide region, and a great area of land is needed to support each individual, compared with that required in an agricultural community. The sparse population is divided into family units which may include twenty persons. Occasionally there may be larger gatherings, since at a season of plenty, when much food can be gathered in a small space, members of different groups may meet. Only on such occasions is there opportunity for the exchange of knowledge and views. However, both knowledge and ideas are likely to be very limited. In small groups there is less opportunity for division of labour apart from that between the sexes, especially when nearly all waking time is needed for food collecting ; and without it technical advance cannot go far.

The tools of savages, to judge by the behaviour of apes today, may first have been sticks ; but by the time of Pekin man stone choppers had long been manufactured. As containers there are gourds and shells and perhaps baskets, but no pottery. For coverings skins, grasses and bark may be used, but there are no textiles. There are no domestic animals, either for food or for draught. There is private property in weapons, digging sticks, collecting bags and trinkets, but not in food.

Neanderthal man—our immediate predecessor in Europe—probably had all these resources. Stone tools were more skilfully made, by flaking, than were those of earlier man ; in particular there were well designed scrapers and points. There were a few bone tools. Traps were made. Burial of the dead suggests some kind of religion or magic, and cannibalism, which was also practised, may have had a similar foundation, since the eating of a person's body is sometimes supposed to confer the strength or virtue of the eaten on the eater.

This summary takes us to the end of the whole of the Lower Palæolithic period, including the period of the Mousterian culture for which Neanderthal man was responsible. ("Palæolithic" means "old stone age".) More information is given in the chart on page 78. In the Upper Palæolithic we come to the stage, called the Higher Savagery, at which our own type, *Homo sapiens,* first appears. As we have seen, a few men remain today in this stage of social development, but in the Mediterranean area certainly, and no doubt in other parts of the world, men lived in this way during a period beginning at least 70,000 years ago and ending perhaps 10,000 years ago. The variety of cultures that existed during this long period is only imperfectly known : large parts of the world are almost unexplored for possible remains, and most of our present knowledge comes from France and the North of Spain ; North Africa has however yielded some valuable material. Even in this small area it is possible to distinguish a series of distinct phases, in each of which the design of tools and clay vessels, artistic styles and mode of life all have characteristic features. The different cultures do not correspond to the different physical types shown by skeletal remains. Thus one culture, called the Gravettian, has left widespread traces in Western Europe ; and it is found that Gravettian equipment was used both by "Cro-Magnon" man—a type regarded as typically "European"—, and by the Grimaldi type which in skull character has been held to resemble a typical negro. Both types are found together in the Guttes de Grimaldi at Mentone.

This fact gives further support to the conclusions on race differences reached in chapters 6 and 7.

H. sapiens, from the first we know of him, had much more elaborate flint tools than his predecessors. After a large fragment had been struck from the main mass much skilled secondary flaking was done to get the desired shape. Bones, antlers and teeth also were used as instruments. Stone lamps, pestles and mortars were made. There was still no pottery, but clay modelling was done. Remarkable works of art, including figurines, are found in the caves used as dwellings, but we do not know what the significance of these works was to palæolithic man. Skins were probably used for clothing, and sinews for bows and harpoon lines. Spears and arrows had flint or bone points.

Thus from the first *H. sapiens* has shown a high level of manual skill, together, perhaps, with an æsthetic sensibility. Nevertheless, for tens of thousands of years man remained in the pre-agricultural phase, and lived by hunting, shooting and fishing, and by the collection of wild plant food and honey. It is likely that, as a rule, there was a seasonal nomadism, in which the movement of the small family groups was determined by the travels of game in search of food and water. In winter, caves, or simple structures with the floor below ground level, were occupied. A typical group would perhaps occupy four or five huts, each housing several people.

The use of well-constructed huts was developed in Europe in the latest pre-agricultural phase. This new phase, the mesolithic, or middle stone age, lasted a relatively short time before it blossomed out into the agricultural revolution. The characteristics which distinguish it from the old stone age are the domestication of the dog for hunting ; the use of nets, hooks and lines for fishing, (but perhaps it is that these have been preserved only from this more recent phase) ; and the construction of canoes, paddles, skis and sledges for transport. There was thus a greater variety of technical skills, but no fundamental difference from the palæolithic. In general, savagery, whether "higher savagery" or not, whether carried on with mesolithic equipment or that of the old stone age, is a precarious existence. It has been calculated that the human population of the world before agriculture was practised may have been no more than 10,000,000—about the number now living within 20 miles of the City of London. England is believed to have had a population of about 200 at that time, and, when agriculture first began, of 2,000. These figures, though little more than guesses based on the known population densities of present-day primitive peoples, at least give some idea of the poverty of human existence before agriculture was invented.

PRIMITIVE BARBARISM

The great change came about 7,000 years ago. At that time cultivation of domestic plants began in the sub-tropical zone which includes North Africa, Syria, Iran and Turkestan ; the whole area today is dry and largely desert, but during the Pleistocene it had had a good rainfall. At first cultivation was no doubt confined to the most favourable regions, such as the Nile valley, where there was plenty of water. The type of cultivation was that called "extensive" : that is, there was frequent breaking of new ground as the old lost its productivity. There was thus a less permanent type of settlement than is found among people practising intensive cultivation—the continued use of the same plots of land for an indefinite period. (Extensive cultivation was still being used in Western Europe after the collapse of Rome.)

No doubt men had already used the seeds of wild grasses as food. Flint sickles found at Mount Carmel suggest that cereals were eaten by the mesolithic cave-dwellers, probably before 6,000 B.C. The first step in agriculture was to induce suitable grasses to grow annually on selected plots within a settlement. In the Mediterranean area two wheats, wild Einkorn and wild Emmer, were domesticated, together with wild barley. (Rye and oats came much later, at first as weeds of wheat and barley fields. Their advantage was their capacity to give good yields in more northern climates than wheat would stand.) The earliest known civilisations, those of Syria, Mesopotamia and the valley of the Indus, occupy an area roughly coinciding with the distribution of the wild ancestors of wheat and barley, and the civilisations of Europe and Western Asia may be said to be founded on the productivity of these two plant species.

DATE	ECONOMIC SYSTEMS (Mode of Production)	TECHNICAL PERIOD (Tools and Materials)	INVENTIONS AND INNOVATIONS
2,000 –	CAPITALISM Wage Labour [Europe and N. America] WESTERN EUROPEAN CIVILISATION	MODERN	INVENTIONS OF MODERN ERA Steam Engine [1781]
1,000 –	FEUDALISM, Serfdom [Europe]		Printing [1381]
		IRON	Crop Rotation
0 –	GRECIAN & ROMAN CIVILISATION		
			Watermill
1,000 –	ANCIENT CIVILISATION Slavery [S. Europe, N. Africa, Middle East especially ; also India, China, Central and South America]	BRONZE	Iron used
2,000 –			
	INDUS CIVILISATION	NEOLITHIC	
3,000 –	FIRST EGYPTIAN AND MESOPOTAMIAN CIVILISATIONS		
			Wheeled Vehicles Plough
4,000 –			Sail
			Copper Smelting
5,000 –	PRIMITIVE BARBARISM i.e. Agriculture and Stock-breeding without cities		STOCK-BREEDING AGRICULTURE
6,000 –		MESOLITHIC	
7,000 –	SAVAGERY		

THE DEVELOPMENT OF HUMAN SOCIETY IN THE WEST
The approximate relations in time of the stages in the development of civilisation, and of some major technical advances. The sequence shown applies mainly to the Mediterranean area and Europe. A chart of this sort necessarily gives only a much simplified picture of what happened ; for sources of more information reference should be made to the bibliography

11

The domestication of animals for food began at about the same time as cereal cultivation. The dog had preceded agriculture, as an adjunct to hunting. Cattle, sheep, goats and pigs were brought in early. The use of the horse, ass, ox and camel for transport and traction came later. The early stages of settled agriculture, with both cultivated cereals and domestic herds, have been most studied at the ancient settlements of Fayum and Merimde in Egypt, and Sumer in Mesopotamia. It is at the latter that the use of sheep's wool for clothing is first recorded, probably 4,000 years before the present era. Dairy farming also seems to have begun in Mesopotamia, perhaps 1,000 years later.

The type of culture associated with the most primitive agriculture is called neolithic—the culture of the new stone age. The Maoris of New Zealand were still at this stage in 1800. Our knowledge of the neolithic phase throughout the world is exceedingly fragmentary, but it is probable that agriculture arose independently in several regions. Certainly it seems that the maize and potato agriculture of Central and South America owes nothing to the ancient Egyptians, and in China that based on millet and the pig may have been a separate development.

Wherever it was adopted agriculture had the most profound effects on human life. Its primary function was to ensure a greater and more reliable supply of food, but in doing so it made possible a vast number of new techniques and activities which, in their combined effects, transformed man from a rare creature into the dominant species that he is today. The earliest agricultural communities were probably ten to twenty times as large as the nomadic groups of savagery. Among the two or three hundred persons specialisation of labour became possible, and this in turn gave rise to more complex and more skilled operations. Among the earliest trades so established were those of the weaver, the potter and the flint polisher. There was at this stage, however, no major technical advance from savagery, apart from the development of agriculture and stockbreeding themselves. The possibility of great technical developments depended, in the first place, on the acquisition of sufficient agricultural skill to produce a *surplus of food* from the soil. An important contribution to farming technique was made by the traction plough—the plough drawn by oxen (or, later, by the horse) : this greatly increased the arable area that one man could cultivate. The use of domestic animals as a source of power was in fact of fundamental importance. Another technique of the greatest value was that of irrigation, which was developed on a large scale in Egypt and Mesopotamia. The immediate consequence of these advances is illustrated at Fayum : in this prosperous peasant community of between 6,000 and 5,000 B.C. there were two groups of silos, numbering 67 and 98 respectively ; each held, on the average, about 8 cwt. of grain, which was probably the yield of two or three acres.

CIVILISATION

Civilisation has been called the culture of cities. Cities are themselves large gatherings of men not engaged on food production. They appear first in the valleys of the Nile in Egypt, the Tigris and Euphrates in Mesopotamia, the Indus in northern India, and perhaps simultaneously the Yangtse-kiang in China. We have seen that an important function of a food surplus is to support workers in crafts and industries other than agriculture and stock breeding. The surplus however does more than that. From very early it was also a basis for trade. Certain important commodities are found only in a few places : raw materials such as flint, and later copper, tin and iron were mined and transported long distances, either in the crude state or in the form of finished products such as axes, vessels, shields or ornaments ; and other consumer goods such as pottery and trinkets entered largely into the trade of early civilisation. Thus human communities became more complex, and came to need a central administration, a legal system and machinery for keeping order and enforcing the law. Cities were the centres, therefore, not only of craftsmanship and trade, but also of administration ; and the food surplus had to support a ruling class of priests and kings who took taxes or tribute in the form of food. This was the origin of the *state*, the apparatus of government and control by a relatively small ruling class.

A series of new discoveries and inventions followed. In the

fourth millenium B.C., that is, between five and six thousand years ago, the wheel was invented, and used both for transport and in the making of pottery. Oversea trade led to the development of the sailing ship, and this in turn to the establishment of navigational methods. Navigation requires a knowledge of the stars, and so is one of the sources of the science of astronomy. The other early source is the needs of agriculture itself, since to plan the sowing of crops according to the seasons a calendar is required. The great pyramid of Egypt is so designed that the dog-star, Sirius, is visible in a central chamber only at the equinoxes. The Egyptians had a year of 365 days and no leap year, and this calendar was probably used first in 4242 B.C. Knowledge of astronomy and of the working of the calendar was no doubt a prerogative of the priest-kings, and since this knowledge was a source of their power, we can guess that they guarded it jealously : they provide an early example of the restriction of learning to a particular class. The association between religion and the calendar is exemplified in England by the famous neolithic temple at Stonehenge, which is so arranged that on midsummer day the sun rises in line with two marked points.

In Egypt the needs of agriculture stimulated the growth also of geometry, owing to the necessity for re-surveying the fields each year after the Nile floods had obliterated all landmarks.

The use of written numbers and alphabetic scripts dates from about 3,000 B.C., and is contemporary with the Asiatic discovery of bronze. At this time the civilisation of the Indus valley had reached a very high level of development. Among the technical problems that arise in all cities are the supply of clean water and the disposal of liquid waste. At the city of Mohenjo-daro, on the River Indus, there was a well-organised system of aqueducts and drains, and there is evidence of deliberate town-planning by the city government.

Civilisation not only creates material wealth and an elaborate technology, but by making leisure possible it leads also to development of the arts. At the same time the media for artistic expression are augmented. The artists of the higher savagery took advantage of the leisure made possible by a plentiful game supply to paint and draw on cave walls and on bone. The artists of civilisation could express themselves also as architects, using inorganic materials for building ; and in Egypt a heptatonic musical scale was invented. In this way, on the basis of a successful agriculture, the main features of all civilisations up to 200 years ago were developed nearly 5,000 years before the industrial revolution in Europe. Even a money economy was established in Mesopotamia.

Between the neolithic phase and the present one is a long period of continuing, relatively slow technical and economic change. Stone implements gradually gave place to metal : at first copper was used, and later tin and copper together, to make bronze ; later still iron, which is more difficult to extract from its ores but far more plentiful, came into general use, and it is only now, in the twentieth century, that other materials such as aluminium are beginning to replace it for some purposes. There were important improvements in power production. First, water power, which began to be used in the late Roman Empire, for such purposes as grinding wheat and separating ores, became very important in some areas ; second, the invention of the horse collar in mediæval times, in place of a strangling yoke, greatly increased the effective muscular power of horses, and, in Bernal's words, "threw open to the plough millions of acres of rolling country." Iron horse shoes also were invented in the middle ages. Bernal goes on :

The miners developed wooden pumps to tap the deeper veins of ore, and spread their activities into the wild mountains of the Ertzgebirge and the Carpathians. The shipwrights introduced the rudder and the practice of sailing into the wind ; and turned the compass, which was borrowed from the Chinese, to good purpose in crossing open sea. Two other borrowings from China were equally important—gunpowder, which gave its users, backed by the metal industry, an immediate military superiority ; and paper and printing, which spread literary culture, personal religion and political consciousness among the whole of the mercantile classes.

Economically, the great iron age civilisations of the Mediterranean—of Italy, Greece, Palestine and North Africa—were based largely on slavery, at least for industrial production.

Productive and other manual work was done by classes sharply marked off as of inferior status, and a relatively small ruling group had the prerogative of administration and access to a good education. The consequent separation of those with clerical knowledge from the people with practical skills had an ill effect on technical and scientific development which is still reflected in administration and education today. In Europe, after the fall of Rome, this system gave place to feudalism, under which the cultivator was typically a serf, limited to working on one particular patch of soil. This led to an increase in the productivity of the soil in the temperate forest area, where regular rotation of crops became customary. It was accompanied by the development of guilds of craftsmen and merchants which led to an improved status for their members.

The conventional account of the middle ages is that given by historians interested primarily in political and perhaps economic history, and in the arts. Here we are concerned rather with techniques, and especially those which played an important part in agricultural and industrial production. Some historians indeed consider that this aspect is a key to the understanding of the period. Farrington quotes an American, Lynn White :

> The cumulative effect of the newly available animal, water and wind power upon the culture of Europe has not been carefully studied. But from the twelfth and even from the eleventh century there was rapid replacement of human by non-human energy wherever great quantities of power were needed or where the required motion was so simple and monotonous that a man could be replaced by a mechanism. The chief glory of the later Middle Ages was not its cathedrals or its epics or its scholasticism : it was the building for the first time in history of a complex civilisation which rested not on the backs of sweating slaves or coolies but primarily on non-human power.

The Scientific Age

Today civilisation has begun a change greater than any of those of the past. It is taking place with remarkable rapidity on the historical time-scale, though with painful slowness for those who live through it. In 1850, in Western Europe, the efforts of three-quarters of the population were needed to provide a food surplus adequate for the remaining quarter not engaged in food production. Today, in advanced areas, the figures are reversed : one quarter produce enough surplus for three-quarters of the population. Thus in such countries as France, the United States and New Zealand (all of which normally export food) 50 per cent of the population live in towns. In Great Britain, which imports food in exchange for manufactured goods, the figure is 80 per cent. On the other hand, in the whole of Asia, where (except in the U.S.S.R.) modern agricultural techniques are hardly practised, only about 15 per cent of the population are reckoned to be town dwellers. The change in agricultural productivity per man is partly a reflexion of the technical advance of industry. The invention of machines which enable us to make use of the energy in coal and oil has made it possible, in the advanced countries, to replace the muscle power, not only of man but now also of domestic animals, by more effective installations. Large numbers of workers have been released from food production, with a great potential increase in material wealth and leisure. This state of affairs is at once based on and has led to the development of our knowledge of the physical sciences. The other basis of modern agriculture is applied biology, of which some features are discussed in the next chapter.

The economic counterpart of these technical developments is capitalism, which had replaced feudalism in most of Europe by the end of the nineteenth century. Under capitalism not only land but also capital goods such as mines, factories and transport services are privately owned ; or if they are not, they are operated by a state which is itself controlled by the owners of large capital installations. It was indeed the single control of big productive units that made the large scale application of modern techniques possible : previously the individual craftsman had often owned his own tools and equipment, but a blast furnace, the machinery for a mine, or a steam loom, could not be worked by single individuals or even by a family ; in practice they were worked by a number of wage-earners and owned by the employer. Today capitalism in its turn has in some countries already been replaced by yet a further economic system, socialism, under which private ownership is restricted to personal property, and the means of production are communally owned and controlled.

None of these phases of human society is the prerogative of any particular biological type. We have seen that this applies to palæolithic cultures. The great invention of agriculture itself seems to have been made separately by widely different groups. Again, the early civilisation of the Indus has been described as the product of "peoples of mixed origin and diverse racial types". The various pre-historic cultures of Europe are often attributed to groups of contrasted physical types, such as "tall long-heads" and "lightly built round-heads". Certainly the various migrant or conquering groups differed on the average in such physical characters as stature or cephalic index, but there was continual intermingling of peoples and exchange of ideas and techniques. In the same way, today, the modern culture originating in western Europe has been absorbed, in many of its features, by such diverse groups as the New Zealand Maoris, the Japanese and formerly primitive peoples in northern Siberia.

In the first nine chapters of this book the topic has been human diversity in time and space : what determines human differences, and the social consequences of the differences. But when we study civilisations and cultures we can look at mankind as an entity—not indeed, because there is any uniformity of cultures, but because wherever he is, and of whatever type, man has certain fundamental problems to solve; and the different kinds of society, with their various types of economy and techniques, are his attempts to solve those problems in the varied circumstances in which he lives. Among these problems are the three great biological ones : the supply of food, which has already been partly discussed in this chapter ; the prevention of infectious disease ; and the maintenance of the population by the bearing of children. These are the subjects of the next four chapters.

CHAPTER II

FOOD AND SOIL

All progress in capitalist agriculture is a progress . . . in the art of robbing the soil ; all progress in increasing the fertility of the soil for a given time is a progress towards ruining the lasting sources of that fertility.

KARL MARX in 1870

One of the most ruinous limiting factors is the capitalistic system—and this is one of the gravest criticisms that can be leveled against it. The methods of free competition and the application of the profit motive have been disastrous to the land. . . .

Throughout virtually the entire world, land is not used to produce the crop best adapted to it on a permanent basis but to produce as much cash as possible, as cheaply as possible and as quickly as possible—the same system exalted by the manufacturer.

WILLIAM VOGT
(Chief of Conservation Section, Pan-American Union) in 1948

NONE of the advances in food production has yet prevented food shortages. Increased food supplies led also to great increases in the density of human populations, and when their food supply fails the disaster is correspondingly great. This sort of thing is familiar enough to the biologist : animal populations are prevented from indefinite increase by *limiting factors,* and food supply is sometimes the factor which determines the maximum size of a population. (Other possible factors are the amount of space for breeding, and the number and efficiency of predators or parasites : for instance, the cats of a village may reduce the maximum population of mice.) Man himself is a limiting factor, or creates such factors, for many animal and plant populations : in the attempt to grow or to capture food for himself he is obliged to reduce the food available for other species, to destroy their living-space and sometimes to kill them directly, either because they themselves provide food or because they interfere with his activities.

There is thus a complex interaction between human populations and the populations of other species, both plant and
animal, in all the regions of the land and sea where man lives
or works. The study of this interaction, which is a part of
the science of ecology, is important for many reasons, including
the fact that it is a necessity for a scientific agriculture. The
need for science in farming has become especially obvious
during the twentieth century. One reason for this is the
increasing consciousness of what scientific method can do,
when it is applied to such problems as the improvement of
soil or the breeding of better strains of crop plants or domestic
animals. A second reason has been the enormous scale of
human food production during this century, accompanying
the increase of human populations in every continent ; these
changes have led to disruption of balanced communities of
animals and plants in many parts of the world, and consequent
loss of soil fertility and other natural resources. Yet a third
reason is that, for the first time, the problem of feeding the
world is being considered as a single problem : as we shall see
in the next chapter, it is now possible to say with some precision
what constitutes an adequate diet, and to show that the great
majority of people in the world do not get one.

This chapter, then, is devoted to the relations of human
populations to their natural environment, and in particular to
the plant and animal communities which are of especial
importance to us as farmers. Among these communities of
living things is the soil itself, largely inanimate but dependent
for its fertility on its living inhabitants. Much of what follows
is devoted to problems and difficulties which have arisen from
the advances of civilisation described in the last chapter.

A Plundered Planet ?

The wealthy civilisations, with their dense populations and
advanced techniques, are a measure of the success of agriculture
in providing a surplus of food beyond the needs of the
producers ; this success is reflected also in the recent rapid
growth of human populations, of which the figures are given in
chapter 14. These expanding human communities have displaced previously existing communities of other species. In

North America, for instance, when European colonisation began, the number of indigenous human beings was of the order of 1m., but there were probably 50m. bison, and vast herds of other large mammals such as elk, deer, caribou, antelope and moose. All these species now exist in only small numbers, or are on the verge of extinction. It is believed that in Canada alone there were 50m. beavers, and this number was reduced to 1m. before protection was introduced. There has been a similar destruction of large mammals in East and South Africa.

More obviously, increasing human numbers, and the expanding need for more agricultural land, have led to the destruction of forests over vast areas. Britain and Western Europe, for instance, were formerly for the most part forest lands except in the higher mountains, but only relatively small wooded patches now remain.

Changes of this sort are, up to a point, inevitable if large human communities are to exist at all. They can, however, lead to further changes which in the long run make a prosperous agriculture impossible. The most serious of these changes are in the soil. If forests are removed from sloping ground in areas of fairly high rainfall, the soil, deprived of its protective covering, is liable to be washed away down to bare, unproductive rock. This is *water erosion*, and it is going on now in great areas of fertile ground in the Americas, Africa and Asia. (Soil erosion must be distinguished from the much slower process of rock erosion referred to in the chapter on evolution.) Another form of water erosion takes place in the plains below the despoiled hills : a result of the destruction of forests is to alter the character of the rivers and streams ; instead of flowing at a relatively even rate they dry up in the dry season and during the rains become raging torrents which cut deep grooves, or gullies, in the soil of the plains.

In the dry season, on the other hand, there is drought : the soil dries and becomes powdery, and may be blown away. The same result often comes from loss of plant cover due to overgrazing. This is *wind erosion*, and the spectacular effects it sometimes produces have made it famous. Osborn describes "the shock that came to the people of America in 1934."

In that year a vast transcontinental dust-laden windstorm, darkening the sun, broadcast the fact that large once-fertile portions of five western states . . . had become a desolate dust bowl. This catastrophe was the result of overgrazing by too large herds of cattle and sheep and of ploughing for crops grasslands that should never have been converted to this use.

H. H. Bennett, another American authority, has said :

In the short life of this country we have essentially destroyed 282m. acres of land, crop and rangeland. Erosion is destructively active on 775m. additional acres. About 100m. acres of cropland, much of it representing the best cropland we have is finished in this country. We cannot restore it.

It takes nature from 300 years to 1,000 years or more to bring back a single inch of topsoil and we sometimes lose that topsoil as the result of a single rain, if it is an especially heavy torrential type of rain.

The first examples of soil destruction have been taken from North America because that area has been very fully studied, and because there the destruction has been exceptionally rapid. But every other continent has suffered erosion, and some extinct civilisations seem to have been helped on their way by the disappearance of their agricultural resources. The Maya civilisation of Guatemala created deserts by the destruction of forests, just as today the soil of Mexico is being washed into the sea as a result of ill-planned attempts to cultivate land on the steep slopes of the mountains. North Africa was once an area of a dominant civilisation, but it is now principally desert ; this could probably have been prevented with a different system of cultivation. The area between the Tigris and Euphrates was once, in Osborn's words, "a land suggestive of the Garden of Eden, a rich land whose people lived well, built flourishing cities, established governments and developed the arts." Its degeneration into desert seems to have been helped by the cutting down of forests, perhaps overgrazing of grassland, and, finally, the wrecking of the irrigation works which coincided with political collapse.

It is not suggested here that the collapse of these ancient civilisations is to be simply explained by defects in their methods of land management. It might indeed be argued that the errors of the farmers should be attributed to imperfections of economic or political organisation, and that these were the significant causes of collapse. Later in this chapter we shall see that the destruction of natural resources today cannot be adequately discussed unless economic, as well as biological, problems are considered. The facts that are fully established are the creation of deserts in once fertile lands by a series of civilised communities, from three thousand years ago up to the present day.

It has been suggested that these calamities have been brought about, not by man's activities, but by climatic influences. It is obvious that climate has played a part, but it is extremely doubtful whether this can anywhere have been a decisive one. Soil erosion occurs only where agriculture is practised ; it follows that climate can be blamed for it only if there have been climatic changes for the worse since agriculture began. There is little evidence for such changes : olive groves can still be made to flourish in North Africa, in the very places where they were cultivated by the Roman colonists ; indeed a few have survived the past two thousand years. Palestine, extensively eroded, can nevertheless support the same crops as were grown in biblical times, given proper care. In India and China there has been much erosion, but alongside the areas of bare rock are terraced and irrigated lands which have been continuously cultivated for three thousand years. Soil erosion cannot be considered as anything but man-made.

The material destruction of soil is the final result of bad land management and much damage can be done before erosion itself occurs. In Africa the Sahara is said to be advancing in some areas at the rate of half a mile a year, but this is only one consequence of the mismanagement of the grass-covered savannahs. The great plains of North Africa, potentially fertile and capable of carrying a prosperous agriculture, have a dry season which is sometimes as long as eight months ; only a carefully preserved plant cover, either of grasses or larger plants, can prevent severe drying and loss of fertility. Excessive grazing by domestic animals (of which the goat is particularly destructive) is in vast areas eating away the plant cover, and ruining the land. From America Vogt gives another example :

> Virgin soils in Ohio, with unimproved seed and no insect control, yielded a hundred bushels of corn per acre, and sixty bushels of wheat. Crops now average forty-two bushels of corn and twenty of wheat. And even this yield per acre in one of the most advanced states in the Union, where there is greatly increased knowledge of disease and pest control, fertilizers and plant breeding, is being maintained with difficulty and at great expense.

THE "BALANCE OF NATURE"

Soil erosion and loss of fertility can be regarded as results of the upsetting of a natural balance or equilibrium. Forests or grassy plains can remain stable for very long periods ; rivers change their character only through millions of years. If there are grazing animals their numbers may be restricted by predators (such as lions), by the water supply or by other limiting factors. Soil losses are made good, probably more than made good, by material derived from dead plants and animals.

Agriculture cannot avoid upsetting this balance of nature. The vital necessity is that it should be replaced by another equilibrium, one chosen by man to suit his own ends. This is not only a matter of preserving the soil : it involves also allowing for the activities of many plant and animal species which are indirectly, and often quite unexpectedly, affected by agriculture. The most obvious of these species are the pests, and especially those which attack crops in the fields. By greatly increasing the growth of some plants, particularly cereals, man has created conditions favourable for the rapid multiplication of various fungi, insects and rodents, many of which had probably been hitherto comparatively rare species.

The most spectacular of the onslaughts on our crops are those due to locusts ; there are seven important species, and between them they cover the Americas, Africa, the Near East, central Asia, India, China, Indonesia and Australia. As new regions are opened to cultivation so are locust swarming grounds multiplied. In the Americas plagues of the related grass-hoppers cause similar damage as well. Other spectacular disasters to field crops are due to field mice : the grain-producing areas of Europe, Asia and North America are subject to periodic plagues of small rodents which do damage on a scale similar to that of locusts. The third main group of pests are the parasitic fungi : the potato blight swept Europe in the nineteenth century and caused the total loss of the potato crop in Ireland in 1846 ; in 1870 another fungus, a leaf rust, wiped out the coffee plantations of Ceylon, and the country was saved from ruin only by the establishment of the tea industry. In Central America and the West Indies the Panama disease has come near to causing the complete destruction of banana cultivation.

These dramatic effects of pests are well enough known, and they are of first-rate importance. But a great proportion of the food losses due to pests goes on continuously and unobtrusively : the pests are there all the time, and they take their regular toll which may amount to 10 or 50 per cent of the total. This is especially the case with the losses of stored food. Food may be stored by peasants in a rolled mat, a bamboo cylinder or a pit in the ground ; by farmers in corn rick or barn; by merchants in warehouse or silo : in all these places the concentration of foodstuffs encourages the multiplication of rats and mice, weevils and other insects, mites, and moulds. So universal are these pests that throughout the world farmers and warehousekeepers often regard their presence as inevitable. World transport has further ensured that, however narrow the original range of a particular species, it has good opportunities of spreading to every country in which suitable conditions exist : the brown spider beetle, as one example, coming probably from Tasmania, has so spread during the past 70 years that it is now found in every grain warehouse in Europe and North America.

These are examples of fairly direct and simple connexions between human activities and changes in animal and plant populations. There are many more complex interactions. In North America agriculture chronically suffers severe losses from small rodents. These pests are preyed on by carnivorous mammals, such as foxes, by birds of prey and by snakes. All these predators have been systematically persecuted by farmers who have thus, in all probability, greatly increased the rodent damage.

Sometimes it is not a question of whether to kill or not to kill. Some farming communities favour the careful preservation of hedgerows and small woodlots, others destroy them ; a point in favour of their preservation is that they are nesting places for small birds which eat injurious insects.

To continue on these lines would be merely to lengthen the list of examples of natural interactions. The further examples could be taken from the management of fisheries and of whaling ; from forestry ; from the control of the living population of the soil ; and from every other department of land or wildlife management. Man is a part of nature, and to achieve satisfactory control of his environment he has to study the whole nexus of relationships in which he is involved.

FEEDING THE WORLD

So far in this chapter the emphasis has been on difficulties and problems. But it would be far from true to suggest that the whole history of food production is one of blunders and mismanagement. There are examples even of very primitive groups in which admirable principles of land management have been applied. In New Guinea some of the mountain dwellers with a neolithic economy use a system of crop rotation combined with terracing which ensures the preservation of the soil and its fertility ; they also use the vegetation for green manure as they clear ground for planting. In the lowlands the neighbouring peoples use a system of ditching which both drains swamps and provides new, unexhausted soil to spread over the surface. In many parts of Africa the Africans have used crop rotations in which leguminous plants are sown at regular intervals to replenish the nitrogen of the soil. The most important principles of land management, such as irrigation and drainage, terracing, manuring and plant selection seem to have been developed independently in the old world and the Americas, some of them before civilisation began in either group of continents.

All the great civilisations have depended on a successful and stable agriculture. We have seen that some, such as those

PLATE 13

GULLY EROSION

Above, an eroded hillside in Jackson, Mississippi. *Below*, erosion in the Tennessee Valley area before conservation began

DUSTBOWL
On the level, almost treeless prairies of North America excessive
wheat growing has led to severe wind erosion

PLATE 14

CONTOUR PLOUGHING
A method of preventing loss of water down slopes. This field in
Oklahoma, U.S.A., is to be planted with cotton

of North Africa and the Near East, collapsed and their agriculture with them. But others have continued. Large areas of China have sustained a stable agriculture for thousands of years, by the use of irrigation, terracing to prevent erosion, and extensive manuring (commonly with human excrement) to preserve fertility. There is however considerable erosion both in China and India. In Western Europe on the other hand the plentiful and evenly distributed rainfall, and the relative flatness of much of the ground, have made possible an even more stable system of cultivation ; moreover, since Western Europe was the original home of modern science, scientific methods have been extensively applied there, and so the productivity both of arable land and animal stocks is very high.

The problem which now faces the whole of humanity is to develop these existing systems so that every human being is adequately fed. How far short of this they fall today can be only roughly estimated ; some of the estimates are given in the next chapter. But there is no doubt that hundreds of millions chronically suffer actual hunger, and even more are malnourished. Moreover the population of the world is increasing at the rate of 20m. a year. The next chapter deals with this problem from the point of view of the needs of human beings as consumers of food. Here we are concerned with production.

The total land surface of the world is 36,000m. acres, but the greater part of this is totally unfit for any form of agriculture at present imagined. The limiting factor is water : the annual rainfall must be at least fifteen inches for cultivation to be possible, and there are difficulties if it is less than eighteen inches ; in equatorial lands, with high evaporation, the necessary minimum rises to forty inches. It is estimated that on this basis about one-third of all land could be cultivated. To what extent is this 12,000m. acres actually used by the ~~1,400m.~~ people—two-thirds of humanity—who live on the land ?

The answers to this question vary with the method of estimation. It is probable that about ten per cent of all land, or less than one-third of the land that could be used, is in fact cultivated, but that only 4 per cent of all land is used for crops

which provide human food :
    of total land surface :

land that could be cultivated	=	34 per cent
land that is cultivated	=	10 per cent
land used for human food	=	4 per cent

These estimates imply that there remain enormous areas still to be opened up, but they are misleading if they are taken to show that it would be easy, within a few years, greatly to increase the world's cultivated area. Two hundred years ago there were vast fertile plains in the New World, Australia and elsewhere, waiting to be ploughed and sown with wheat. Today all the easy ground has been occupied (and much of it, as we have seen, plundered) ; a great deal of what remains is tropical forest.

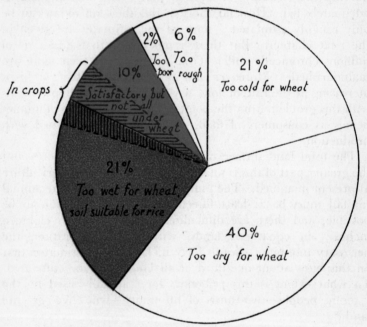

CHARACTERISTICS OF EARTH'S LAND AREA

Despite the difficulties, attempts are already being made to cultivate the tropics. Modern machinery, such as bulldozers, and the new insecticides, have helped to make such projects feasible. One scheme, which has had a good deal of publicity in Britain, was to clear 3.2m. acres in Tanganyika, Rhodesia and Kenya and to plant the areas with ground-nuts for the production of edible fat (of which there is a serious world shortage). Under the original plan there was to have been an annual production of 600,000 tons of ground-nuts by 1951, but this estimate proved to be too optimistic, and the scheme has come in for some severe criticism. But the important question is : are schemes of this sort practical, and can they contribute to the world's food within, say, the 1950's ? Even if it is true that the authorities initiated the ground-nuts scheme without adequate preparation, we may reflect that governments are more usually attacked for procrastination and lack of initiative than for impetuosity. Some of the difficulties of this East African scheme are however of general significance. It is proposed, for instance, that as an alternative to ground-nuts in some areas, sunflowers should be grown and oil extracted from their seed. And the question has been raised whether the bees, necessary for the pollination of the sunflowers, will be present in sufficient numbers ; this depends on conditions in the surrounding terrain, and these have to be studied by biologists before an answer can be given. Here again we have an example of the necessity for studying the whole living nexus, if an efficient agriculture is to be achieved.

On the general prospect of the use of forest lands a recent report of the Food and Agriculture Organisation is optimistic :

Here is virtually a new continent, the unused forest, equal in area to the whole of Asia (excluding the U.S.S.R.), which remains to be explored and used for human benefit. These forests could contribute not only fuel and lumber but also by chemical transformation, pulp, plastics, sugar, ethyl alcohol, yeast and fodder cellulose. It may be that in time they will provide a large proportion of the world's clothing materials and animal feeding stuffs, thus releasing important areas of cropland for food crops.

When the attempt is made to develop a backward area, or even, perhaps, an advanced one, special problems may arise with the human population. At first sight it might appear that a big productive scheme would be certain to benefit the native inhabitants of the area, but in fact it can do so only if their customs and needs are properly considered. Primitive customs are quite unadapted to modern, large-scale agriculture. It follows that, unless a policy of ruthless exploitation and contempt for native needs and abilities is adopted, all such schemes must include provision for the education and general raising of the living standards of the people.

The need for the planning of an area as a whole, and for ensuring that those taking part do so willingly and with knowledge of its value to themselves, has been recognised in a number of big schemes of land development in advanced countries. Of these the Tennessee Valley Authority is an example of what modern engineering can do to make soil fertile by irrigation, provided that all possible means are used for the development of the area, including education and financial help. Similar schemes have been proposed for the Missouri Valley, for the Jordan River in Palestine, for various Indian rivers, for the Niger River in French West Africa, and for a number of others. The Amazon Basin is the subject of a United Nations plan.

The biggest scheme of all is the one begun during the 1930's in a vast area of the U.S.S.R. A very large part of the Soviet Union is too cold for ordinary agriculture (which is why so much work has been done there on cold resistant wheats and other crops) ; and of the remaining land much is liable to severe drought. The remedy in the dry areas is irrigation, and this is planned on an unprecedented scale. The Volga River is to be harnessed, so that the spring flow, which is equivalent to 70 per cent of the annual flow, will be stored and used throughout the season of growth. This however would cause a lowering of the level of the Caspian Sea, into which the Volga flows : ports would find themselves some distance inland, and the fishing industry would be ruined. More water is therefore needed in the Caspian, and this is to be supplied by the partial diversion of some of the rivers of the north, which up to now have flowed into the Arctic Ocean. Part of the trouble in the Volga River area arises from the extensive cutting down of

forests which took place before the revolution, and large
schemes of replanting, including an 800 mile belt of trees along
the Ural river, have now been begun. Even the Don River
may be brought into the scheme ; Osborne writes :

> This plan also had its complications and could only be
> adopted if it were found that the Don could spare enough
> water and still retain an adequate supply for its own various
> functions, including navigation, water supply for the
> cities lying along its course, and even the protection of the
> shellfish beds in the Sea of Azov at the Don's mouth that
> would not survive any material change in water conditions.
> Consideration for even the aquatic resources, a not unimport-
> ant source of food supply, is typical of the care that
> the Russians have taken to observe all of the interrelated
> factors that are involved. All in all it is a project of titanic
> proportions.

As this book goes to press new progress with the scheme is
reported. The two northward flowing rivers, the Ob and
Yenisei, have been dammed, and a channel cut to join them.
The most difficult task was to cut the channel by which their
waters would flow into the Ural river, which itself flows into
the Caspian. This has now been done by means of an "atomic"
explosion. It seems possible that 1949 will be remembered
as the year of the first use of atomic energy to aid in
food production.

The Improvement of Agriculture

Although vast schemes of conservation and development are
essential, they are not the only means of increasing food production. Throughout the world agricultural methods remain
for the most part primitive, and without increasing the cultivated
area or any drastic change of method production could be
greatly raised. The output of food per man in advanced
countries is estimated by the Food and Agriculture Organisation to be about ten times what it is in the backward lands.
The population of the backward areas is nearly three-quarters
of the world's total. In Britain the productivity per acre and the
output per man are three or four times higher than even the more
backward areas of Europe ; and on the average about four

times as much milk is produced by each cow. Yet even British farming could be improved, since the best farms, in which every advantage is taken of technical improvements, have a productivity twice that of the average.

The general, all-round raising of the standards of cultivation depends on the systematic improvement of every aspect of farming practice. Improvement is needed, and is practicable, in the plants and animals themselves ; in the fertility of the soil ; and in the control of weeds and of animal and fungal pests. + the number of machines + design used

The milk yields of many herds, even in Western Europe and the U.S.A., can be doubled in two generations by proper breeding ; such breeding can be greatly accelerated by the use of artificial insemination, which enables the best bulls to serve at least ten times as many cows as would otherwise be possible. The scope for improvement in the wretched cattle of the backward areas of the East is far greater. Besides the improvement of stock by breeding much can be done by better feeding, for instance by the development of pasture of higher quality. Indeed, breeding and the improvement of stock management must go together, since breeding can be done effectively only if a suitable environment can be provided for the herd. The development of the grasslands themselves also depends partly on genetical methods : in the past it has been usual to regard "grass" as a natural phenomenon not much amenable to human interference, but today, on the best pastures, it is treated like any other crop : special seed mixtures are used, selected for the particular conditions of soil and climate, with corresponding improvement of the sward and of the live-stock that feed on it.

The use of special seed from selected plants is one of the most important means of raising crop production generally. A famous example is hybrid maize. The usual method of pre-serving a good strain of a plant or animal species is to inbreed among individuals of the strain (as was described in chapter 2) so as to preserve the favourable genetical qualities ; but if this is done with maize a loss of yield results. Inbred lines are therefore grown only by seedsmen in breeding stations : to produce the seed for the farmer the inbred lines are crossed, and the hybrid seed is distributed for use on the farms, where it gives a high yield. Hybrid maize has made possible yields 25 per cent. higher than before, and more than 90 per cent. of the maize now sown in the Corn Belt of the United States is hybrid.

Breeding is capable of producing not only improved varieties, but quite new types with unexpected combinations of characters. Much has been done on these lines in the U.S.S.R. (There is a story of some botanists trying to develop a radish-cabbage hybrid : they succeeded, only to find that the new plant had the leaves of a radish and the root system of a cabbage. Fortunately, further effort gave the desired result.) The most remarkable of the new hybrids is perennial wheat, a result of crossing wheat with wild couch grass. One variety, known as 34085, is drought-resistant, fungus-resistant and has an exceptionally high gluten content. It is not cold-resistant, but can be grown in the southern areas of the U.S.S.R. where wind erosion is serious and the protection of a perennial covering for the soil is most needed. It can give at least two crops a year, and of course does not require annual sowing.

A better known example of the possibilities of plant breeding is the production of highly productive wheats which are also resistant to the fungus disease called stem rust, which is exceedingly destructive in North America.

Much more of this sort of work remains to be done : research on rice, which is the staple food of at least one third of mankind, is far behind that on the wheats and on maize, though what has been done has given valuable results in India, where experimental farms have a productivity twice that of the average. Research on millet, another important staple of the East, has hardly begun.

If we turn to the improvement of the soil we find a similar picture of much valuable knowledge imperfectly applied, combined with the need for yet more knowledge. The importance of fertilisers and manures is very well known : nearly every gardener uses both inorganic fertilisers and manure derived from a compost heap (which may have been chemically treated) or possibly from the leavings of horses in the street outside. Primitive systems of cultivation, as we have seen, relied on human and animal manure, and on plant residues, to replenish essential elements taken from the soil by their crops. We must still do the same, and on a larger scale ; the sewage from the great cities is a valuable source of manure, and far too little is returned to the fields. But we can supplement the organic manures with synthetic nitrogenous substances : it has been estimated that in Britain the addition of one hundredweight of ammonium sulphate to each acre of average arable land can increase the yield of wheat by nearly two-and-a-half hundredweight. To get the best results potassium and phosphate must be added as well. In advanced countries such practices are commonplace, but over the greater part of the world they remain almost unused. The quality as well as the quantity of plants can be improved by synthetic nitrogenous fertilisers. For instance, the protein content of grass can be doubled, with corresponding benefit to the livestock that feed on it.

Recently, there have been important refinements in our knowledge of soil chemistry. In large areas of Australia a serious condition of livestock, called pining disease, was found to be due to a mineral deficiency of the soil which affected the plants of the pasture and through them the grazing animals. The element that was deficient was not any of these well known to be important, such as nitrogen, phosphorus or potassium, but a comparatively rare one, cobalt. Since then similar phenomena, involving several elements besides cobalt, have been found in many parts of the world ; even in Britain cobalt deficiency has been found, in the words of one writer, "from as far south as Bodmin Moor in Cornwall, to as far north as Ross-shire in Scotland. Few things are more spectacular than the recovery to full health of 'pining' animals after a trace of cobalt has been provided."

We are however only at the beginning of a systematic knowledge of the effects of soil chemistry and physics on plant growth. We still do not know why some plants ("lime lovers") can grow only on alkaline soil, while others must have acid soil. Even the significance of humus for plant growth is controversial. And apart from these general problems every type of soil presents its own difficulties, and requires its own system of manuring.

Care of the soil requires more than attention to its chemistry. *Irrigation* may be needed to prevent excessive dryness and consequent loss of fertility and eventual wind erosion. Irrigation is indeed one of the oldest means of preserving soil fertility. The Nile valley is probably the oldest irrigated area in the world, but in the last half-century it has nevertheless been extensively developed, and the system changed from basin irrigation, or one-crop agriculture based on the annual flooding, to perennial irrigation which allows the growing of several crops a year. For some months in each year no Nile water enters the sea direct : the sea receives only water that has been pumped from the main drains after passage through the irrigated soil. India, with 70m. acres, has the largest irrigated area of any country, three times the area in the United States. There is nevertheless need for much more irrigation in India, and still more elsewhere, and the great river valley plans are largely based on schemes of irrigation.

Erosion is controlled also by preventing loss of plant cover due to overgrazing, by the planting of woods and forests to act as wind breaks, and by special techniques such as ploughing along the contours of hills to prevent a too rapid drainage of water down the slopes. Even beavers have been pressed into service in North America : in areas where water erosion was serious small numbers of beavers have been introduced and allowed to build dams. In one area, where water erosion and flooding were causing loss of orchard trees, twelve beavers were released ; two years later sixty new dams had been built and the flooding greatly reduced. Beavers have been used also to conserve water for irrigation.

The various methods of soil conservation are capable of bringing dramatic improvement in regions where bad management has not gone too far. It is now reported, for instance, that even in the notorious dust bowl of North America agricultural production is higher than ever before.

The very fertility of cultivated soils, however, gives rise to special problems : having made soil fertile we inevitably encourage the growth of unwanted species as well as crop plants. But weed control has recently made great strides : it has been found that substances, sometimes called plant growth hormones, which in some conditions can be used to stimulate the growth of parts of plants, can also be used as selective weed-killers ; by destroying the unwanted species but leaving the crop plant unharmed they can double the yield per acre on some agricultural land.

We have already seen that, just as fertile ground attracts weeds, so does the accumulation of food on cultivated land and in stores attract animal and fungal pests. Here again we are not obliged to resign ourselves to extensive losses : much has been done to enable us to prevent them. The detailed study of the way of life of particular pests has in many instances made possible their large scale destruction. Locusts have for thousands of years made their inexplicable and unpredicted descents on cultivated land, leaving starvation behind them. Only since the first world war has it been found that, when they are not swarming, locusts live as harmless grasshoppers of different appearance from that of the swarming phase. Swarms develop only in certain limited outbreak areas, and are induced partly by climatic influences, some of which are known. It is now possible to predict outbreaks before they occur, and by the use of new insecticides, such as gammexane, the swarms can be intercepted and destroyed before they do any harm. In the early 1930's swarms from a single outbreak area near the Middle Niger swept over nearly the whole of Africa, and did enormous damage. During the 1940's similar outbreaks threatened ; but by that time a control organisation existed, and for the first time in history Africa survived a period of locust attack without serious loss.

The example of locust control is one of many. Although there are serious pests which we are still quite unable to control, and much research remains to be done, for many species the deficiency is not so much in knowledge as in application : there is, for instance, no locust control organisation in South America comparable to that in Africa.

Agriculture and Society

The facts of this chapter show that man's relationship with his environment, and especially with the food-producing part of it, is continually changing. Some of the changes are for the worse, but we have the knowledge to prevent them ; the scope of possible change for the better is incalculably great. It follows that calculations, such as those which purport to deduce the amount of arable land per head necessary for a satisfactory standard of living, can have little validity. There is one much quoted statement, based on North American practice, that the area needed is 2.5 acres to each person ; the actual amount of arable land in the world has been variously estimated at from just over one, to nearly two, acres per head. But since climate, crops, land and farming methods vary enormously from time to time, from country to country, and even from farm to farm, such statements have little real significance.

These calculations will have even less point if completely new methods of food production are introduced on a large scale. It has long been possible to produce sugar from wood shavings by a method known as the Bergius process ; other foodstuffs, including protein, could be made from coal ; the cost is very high, though it is likely that it could be reduced with further research. Another possible way of producing food without soil is by farming the sea. At present about 2 per cent of all food-energy is derived from the sea or fresh waters, but this proportion might be greatly increased by various means. In some pioneer experiments the addition of inorganic salts to sea water has made possible the growth of larger populations of edible fish : the salts, which correspond to the artificial fertilisers used by farmers, promote the growth of microscopic plants, and the plants form the food either of the fish themselves, or of small animals which are in turn eaten by fish. Another way of using the plants of the sea is even more promising, though more elaborate : the plants would be grown either in shallow coastal basins with plenty of sun, or in miles of transparent, plastic piping laid over sunlit deserts, into which sea-water would be pumped. By controlling the conditions in which they grow it is possible to influence the food substances manufactured by the plants : in some conditions certain species can produce a very high fat content. The final product might be used for animal feeding stuffs, and so release arable land for the growing of bread grains ; fats might be used even for human food.

The importance of these novel suggestions is that they illustrate the unlimited possibilities of technical advance. Given a practical problem, however vast, we are quite justified in turning confidently to the methods of science to solve it. As we shall see repeatedly in the next three chapters the most formidable obstacles often arise only when the main technical difficulties have been overcome, and when the application of the new knowledge becomes a task for the whole community.

For scientific knowledge to be applied fully it is not enough to have a few scientists, however, well endowed with money and ability, working on the problems. Large organisations have to be created, staffed in part by technically trained men and women, who can transmit the results of research to the public in general, or to particular sections such as the farming community. Nor is the relationship a simple one of the scientists telling the technicians, and the technicians telling the public. The flow of ideas is in both directions. Laboratory research is essential, but a great part of scientific agriculture has to be worked out in the fields or milking sheds themselves. If it is to be done on an adequate scale the farmer must not only be ready to accept sound methods when they have been worked out : he must be prepared to make an actual contribution, by recording the results of applying new methods or by taking part himself in large scale experiments.

Organisations for large scale research and application are most successful when they operate as part of a general economic advance. A report of the Food and Agriculture Organisation has said :

The over-all objective is to raise real incomes, for otherwise the consumption goals cannot be realised. A given level of food consumption is a direct function of a certain level of income. Although studies in this direction are in their infancy it can be roughly estimated that an increase of 40 per cent in per caput food expenditure in a low-income country would normally be associated with an increase of 40 to 50 per cent in real income. . . . There is here a job of economic engineering—to increase real income per person in the low income countries by at least 50 per cent in a short period of time and, in doing so, to maintain a balance between industry and agriculture appropriate to the country in question.

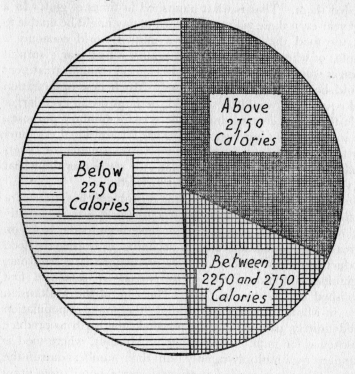

STARVATION

The relative numbers of people in the world at different levels of Calorie intake ; only the one-third (approximately) above 2750 have enough to eat

It is however not enough for action to be taken on a national scale. Mankind can be adequately fed only if the problem is faced as a single one for the whole world. The existence of F.A.O. reflects the understanding of this fact. Before the second world war, among the absurdities of world economic disorganisation was the fact of mass starvation and malnutrition side by side with the deliberate destruction of food, such as wheat and oranges, in producing countries : the food destroyed could not be sold at a profit, and so it was considered better by the producers to let piles of oranges rot, under the eye of an armed guard, rather than to distribute them to those who needed them. That is what happened in times of glut. In a bad year even those who could afford to pay might be unable to get the food they wanted. In a unified world economy a surplus of wheat would be stored against a bad year ; surplus oranges would be canned, probably as juice. Similar treatment would be given to other surpluses. Much new organisation and equipment would be required, perhaps on an even larger scale than that created during the war for military purposes. Up to the present however the pressure for a rational economy has failed to prevent complaints in North America of "over-production" of food : by 1949 plans for restricting the wheat harvest were once again being put forward.

In some people knowledge of these problems has induced a profound pessimism. Since the second world war apparently authoritative predictions of disaster have been made, based on increases of population and a declining or stationary food production. The history of such predictions is a long one, beginning with the *Essay on the principle of population* first published by Malthus in 1798. The core of the Malthusian view, in Malthus' own words, is that "the power of population is indefinitely greater than the power in the earth to produce subsistence for man." According to Malthus, where food is abundant men multiply rapidly until their numbers outrun the food supply ; where food is already scarce, populations grow little, or not at all. These statements, as we have seen, can sometimes be applied to animal populations in nature ; the question is, to what extent do they apply to man ? During the nineteenth century, at least in the western world, they seemed to have no application : the increase in the world's agricultural land and the improvement of agricultural techniques outstripped population growth. Nevertheless in 1898, at a famous meeting of the British Association, the president, Sir William Crookes, pointed to the exhaustion of easily cultivated lands which remained to be opened up, and predicted famine if yields were not increased. Unlike Malthus, however, Crookes suggested a way out : his solution was a vast increase in the use of nitrogenous fertilisers. This increase was in fact achieved, with valuable results for many crops, though it did not make much contribution to raising the yield of wheat.

Today, faced with formidable difficulties, both biological and economic, we can adopt one of two attitudes. We can conclude that there is nothing to look forward to but widespread famine and tens of millions of deaths from starvation and disease, and that the Malthusian dilemma of limited food and unchecked reproduction is insoluble in the foreseeable future ; or we can admit the difficulties, agree that famine threatens in many parts of the world (as it has threatened for the past seven thousand years), yet nevertheless deny that this state of affairs need continue : the technical difficulties can be overcome ; the economic system can be changed.

Unmitigated gloom is rarely found among those who are actually trying to produce more food. We have seen something of the biological advances already achieved, or possible. Of equal importance are the advances in social and economic organisation. The great schemes of land development and conservation, described earlier, demand unified planning and administration which can be done only by governments. A fully mechanised agriculture, making use of every means to raise production, is impossible in a system of peasant farming, with small farms worked, as a rule, by primitive means under a heavy burden of debt. The most drastic and far-reaching changes in farming economics, in response to these needs, have been those of the U.S.S.R. Here all land ownership is vested in the state, and most cultivated land is leased to groups of farmers. Each farm is run as a co-operative society, or collective, by a committee elected from among those who work on it. In 1940 the average number of families on a collective farm was about 80. A proportion of the produce is sold to the state at a fixed price, the rest consumed on the farm or sold in open market. The income of the farm, in cash or kind, is distributed among the workers in accordance with the amount of work done, after deductions for a general fund which covers maintenance, administration, and new construction from cow-sheds and communal nurseries to power-stations. Advisory organisations, seed production and services such as those provided by tractor stations are run by the state, as they are to some extent in many western countries, including Britain. Outside the U.S.S.R. collective systems of various kinds are being developed in Eastern Europe and in China.

It is a commonplace that we are living in a period of drastic and rapid social change. This fact is reflected in the contemporary transformation of world agriculture, from a system largely of small-scale peasant farming with primitive methods, to one of communal farming in which full use is made of scientific knowledge. What Sir John Russell has called "the shrill sensationalism of some of the pessimistic writers" is a product of emphasising only one feature of the contemporary scene. We must accept that feeding the world presents great difficulties, which can be overcome, on the most optimistic estimate, only after decades of effort. Nevertheless the effort has already begun ; existing biological and economic knowledge can take us a great distance if it is applied, and it can be rapidly increased. To the extent that we fail, the failure will be a social and political one, and not a consequence of something inherent in nature and unalterable.

PLATE 15

SOIL CONSERVATION

Above, the result of uncontrolled erosion in Texas, U.S.A. *Below*, the eroded area has been planted with a cover crop which binds the drifting sands

PLATE 16

TERRACING
Rice fields in Java, where terracing prevents washing away of
the soil

CHAPTER 12

FOOD AND NUTRITION

ONE of the scientific triumphs of the twentieth century has been the growth of our knowledge of nutrition. Although much important detail remains to be learnt, it is already possible for a well-advised government to have a national food policy with a scientific basis, or for a well-informed housewife to plan her family's meals scientifically.

THE QUESTION OF QUANTITY

The first problem to be solved is the total quantity of food required. A normal person needs no telling whether he is eating enough : hunger is the guide. There is some individual variation, especially in relation to weight, but on the whole the amount needed depends on the type and quantity of the work done. In this respect our bodies can quite legitimately be compared with a railway locomotive using coal, or an automobile petrol, in proportion to distance travelled or to speed. The energy value of food is measured in Calories. (A Calory is the amount of heat needed to raise one kilogram of water from 15 to 16° C.) An adult of average weight lying in bed, and taking no exercise at all, needs about 1,700 Calories a day to prevent loss of weight. This is the basic quantity needed to keep us going at the lowest level of activity. An hour's light work, such as typing or sewing, adds about 75 Calories to the basic need. An hour's housework or slow walking may add between 75 and 150. A man like a coal-miner, doing very hard physical work, requires 300 Calories or more for each hour, and in many countries men doing heavy work receive extra rations of such foods as bread and cheese.

Chemically there are three types of foodstuff that supply us with energy. (A fourth, alcohol, in the form of wine, has been reckoned to provide Frenchmen and Italians each with an average of about 100 Calories a day, but most nations are less fortunate.) First there are the *carbohydrates*, of which the most important are starch (the main constituent of cereals and

181

potatoes), and sugar. In practice, whether most people have enough to eat depends on whether they have enough starch. Wheat, rye and rice (the first two largely in the form of bread), supply, in an average year, enough Calories for more than half the population of the world. Barley, maize, oats and millet are eaten in large amounts, but far too much of them today is lavished on poultry and other livestock, to produce only a relatively small yield of expensive eggs and meat. Food given to animals loses about 90 per cent of its calorific value before it becomes meat or eggs.

The second type of foodstuff, *protein*, provides, weight for weight, roughly as much energy as carbohydrate. But it is much less important for most people as a source of energy. The main sources of animal protein are meat, fish, cheese and eggs ; milk too is important. Plant protein is eaten mainly in pulses and whole cereals. An adult can do with very little protein indeed, but he can, if necessary, manage on a diet of which almost all the solid is protein : this is what men who depend on hunting have to do. We need, too, very little of the third main type of foodstuff, the *fats*, provided we have plenty of palatable carbohydrate. Fat however provides about twice as much energy per pound as protein or carbohydrate and is therefore a more concentrated form of energy food. Today, in 1949, there is a world shortage of fats. Apart from the fact that this is one aspect of the general shortage of food, fat shortage affects us in two important ways : first, it may reduce our intake of the fat-soluble vitamins, A and D, which we discuss below ; second, it makes it more difficult to prepare palatable meals. The traditional sources of fat in the west are butter and cheese, and meat, but vegetable fats are becoming more important. They have long been in general use in, for instance, large parts of India.

Carbohydrate, fat and protein are needed, not only as energy-givers, but for the growth and maintenance of the body tissues. In this respect protein is of especial importance. It is possible for children to suffer protein deficiency where there is no over-all food shortage. The term "protein deficiency" is, however, imprecise. There are many proteins, and each has a different chemical composition and so a different nutritive value. It has therefore become customary to distinguish "second-class" plant protein from "first-class" animal protein. This is a very crude classification : some animal proteins, notably gelatin, hardly deserve to be called first-class on any scheme ; and the value of plant proteins—which we get mainly from whole wheat, peas, beans and lentils—depends partly on what other protein is being eaten. There are two important practical points. First, growing children, and pregnant and nursing mothers, have a special need for protein, and so should have first call on proteinous foods of animal origin : milk, meat and fish, cheese and eggs. (Men doing heavy work have no special, physiological need for protein. They may however be dissatisfied with meatless meals in a country such as England, with a long tradition of a heavy consumption of beef, mutton and pork or bacon. The justification for extra cheese for heavy workers is that it provides, owing to its high fat content, a considerable amount of energy in a form easily put in a sandwich.) Second, if children and mothers throughout the world are to have adequate diets there must be an enormous increase in milk production. Milk, as everyone knows, is the most complete of all single foods, and it is an excellent source of protein of high nutritive value.

Minerals and Vitamins

There are certain other obvious dietary necessities. Bones and teeth are made largely of calcium phosphate, and so calcium and phosphorus are both required. Milk and cheese are excellent sources of both. In Britain today the most widespread nutritional deficiency is of calcium. Iron is another chemical element easily identifiable in the body, and particularly in the blood : lack of it causes one type of anæmia. Infants and young women are especially liable to be short of it, and after calcium it is the dietary component of which we are most likely to be deficient. Meat, fruit, vegetables and whole flour are important sources. Iodine, as we saw in chapter 2, is also an essential element. Even sodium chloride, the common salt of our tables, is a serious problem in many countries, particularly in the tropics where the heat causes much salt loss in sweat. In the past it has been an expensive

Table 2

THE MAIN TYPES OF FOODSTUFF

Needed in Large Amounts		
	MAIN SOURCES	SPECIAL FUNCTION IN BODY
PROTEIN	Meat, fish, eggs, milk, cheese ; peas, beans, lentils, wheat	Especially important in growth ; also a source of energy
CARBOHYDRATE	Cereals and cereal products ; sugar ; potatoes	Main source of energy for most of world's population
FAT	Meat, butter, cheese, margarine	Twice the fuel value per unit weight of carbohydrate or protein ; contains fat-soluble vitamins
WATER		

"Minerals" : Needed in Smaller Amounts		
CALCIUM .. PHOSPHORUS (as phosphate)	Milk, cheese	Make up a large part of the constituents of bone and teeth
IRON	Vegetables, fruit, whole wheat	Contained in hæmoglobin (the red pigment of blood)
IODINE	Most foods	Contained in the thyroid hormone

All these elements are found in every cell of the body, as well as in the tissues mentioned.

continued

Table 2—*continued*

Vitamins : Needed in Very Small Amounts			
	MAIN SOURCES	GROSS LACK CAUSES :	MINOR LACK CAUSES :
A	Fish-liver ; milk, butter, eggs ; green vegetables	Keratomalacia ; xerophthalmia	Night-blindness (one kind) ; less growth in young
D	Fish-liver ; milk, butter, eggs	Rickets (children) ; osteomalacia (adults)	Inadequate bone growth
B1 (THIAMIN)	Whole wheat ; meat ; yeast	Beri-beri	Nervous disorder ; fatigue
RIBOFLAVIN	As B1	Degeneration of cornea of eye	Inflammation of lips and mouth
NICOTINIC ACID	As B1	Pellagra	Nutritional diar-rhoea
C (ASCORBIC ACID)	Citrous fruits, to-matoes ; other fresh fruit and vegetables	Scurvy	Anæmia ; slow healing of wounds

There are other vitamins, most of them of less practical importance.

(and heavily taxed) commodity even in western Europe.

Carbohydrates, fats and proteins, the "minerals" mentioned in the last paragraph and water : these are obvious necessities. However, if a diet consisting only of these materials in a pure form is given to animals such as young mice, the animals stop growing, sicken and die. On the other hand if a small amount of milk is added the animals survive and grow. Milk makes this difference because it contains several further substances which are essential for life : these, the *vitamins*, are present, and are needed, only in very small amounts.

Table 2 lists the most important vitamins, the effects of deficiencies, and the principal foods in which the vitamins occur. Most large human populations show a high incidence of serious vitamin deficiency diseases. In some of the densely populated areas of Asia beri-beri is common because the principal food is rice without the husk : this supplies starch without B vitamins, and beri-beri is due mainly to extreme vitamin B1 deficiency. In beri-beri the heart is affected, there are muscular spasms and weakness, and unless suitable food is given death results. Another disease with a high incidence in India is xerophthalmia, due to vitamin A deficiency ; the eyes are affected, and the disease is a common cause of blindness ; it is often fatal. A third disease, pellagra, is common in the south of the U.S.A. especially among the negroes, and in south-eastern Europe. It is due to lack of another of the B vitamins. The skin becomes scaly and sores develop ; once again, it may be fatal.

The two other outstanding deficiency diseases, scurvy (vitamin C deficiency), and rickets (vitamin D deficiency), are more likely to occur in northern climates. Vitamin C is found particularly in certain fruits, notably oranges and lemons, and in fresh vegetables. Scurvy has in the past been common in western European towns in late winter. It is fatal in extreme cases, notably among infants. At one time it was called "the London disease". England, indeed, in spite of its thriving agriculture, has a bad reputation for deficiency conditions. Rickets used to be called "the English disease", and certainly until well after the first world war gross rickets was widespread among the children of workers in the large towns. Today the value of fish liver oils has become known to almost everyone, and serious rickets is uncommon, though some degree of calcium deficiency is still general among our children. It is rarer in sunnier climates because vitamin D is formed in the skin by the action of sunlight.

A result of the knowledge of vitamins acquired during the twentieth century has been to increase the demand for certain foods. Fruits that supply vitamin C have entered more and more into world trade, and their production has increased. The other important water-soluble vitamins, those of the B group, occur particularly in whole wheat, whole rice, oatmeal and potatoes, and emphasis has come to be placed more on these than on the more purified forms of carbohydrate such as white flour and sugar. This is of especial importance because the amount of B vitamins required varies with the amount of

	Cereals	Roots and Tubers	Sugar	Fats	Peas and Beans	Fruit and Vegetables	Meat	Milk
DENMARK	4 lb.	4 lb. 10 oz.	2 lb. 5 oz.	1 lb. 3 oz.	1 oz.	5 lb. 1 oz.	2 lb. 15 oz.	4½ U.S. quarts
JAVA	5 lb. 4 oz.	6 lb. 1 oz.	3 oz.	1½ oz.	1 lb. 10 oz.	2 lb. 8 oz.	5 oz.	Negligible
NEW ZEALAND	2 lb. 11 oz.	1 lb. 14 oz.	2 lb. 1 oz.	14 oz.	1 oz.	5 lb. 15 oz.	5 lb. 15 oz.	4 U.S. quarts
DOMINICAN REPUBLIC	2 lb. 14 oz.	11 lb. 2 oz.	10 oz.	3 oz.	13 oz.	3 lb. 15 oz.	1 lb. 4 oz.	¼ U.S. quart

STARVATION AND MALNUTRITION. A comparison of two wealthy, food-producing countries with two poor ones

Food in four countries before the second world war. A comparison of two wealthy, food-producing countries with two poor ones carbohydrate eaten. As for the fat soluble vitamins, vitamin A (or a substance that becomes vitamin A in the body) is fairly easily obtained from green vegetables and from carrots, although this has not prevented a good deal of mild vitamin A deficiency among the poor in England. And both A and D are found in liver, the fat of meat, fat fish such as herrings, eggs, and butter. They are also now added in small quantities to margarine in the United Kingdom.

Beyond all these foods in importance is milk. Every essential nutrient, with the possible exception of vitamin C, is found in useful amounts in cows' milk, and anybody over the age of a few months can digest it.

What People Eat

In the period between the wars most of the discussion about food dealt with vitamins and perhaps minerals, and the general need for improving the *quality* of diets. In the next section we shall see the reason for this. But today, as we have seen, the Food and Agriculture Organisation of the United Nations is primarily concerned with the quantity of food in the world. This problem is not a new one : it is not only a result of war followed by world-wide drought. In the 1930's Europe, with a population just over one-third that of Asia, consumed appreciably more cereals and more than six times as much meat as the whole of the peoples of Asia. This is a measure of the inadequacy of the food available to more than half the world's population living in Asia. If similar figures were available for dairy products there is no doubt that the disparity would be found to be even greater. Yet, as we shall see, diet even in some of the better-fed European countries was grossly deficient for large sections of the population.

Let us consider the position in the 1930's in some of the main countries. The areas of greatest deficiency, according to a report by F.A.O., were Central America and most of Asia. But parts of South America and of Africa, on which there is less information, were probably as bad. Some useful dietary surveys have been carried out in *India*. (In this book "India" is a geographical expression, and includes Pakistan). For the

majority of the population rice is the staple food, though some
eat other cereals as well, and in the north, notably the Punjab,
wheat and millet are eaten. On the whole the rice eaters have
little or no fresh fruit or green vegetables ; about 50 per cent
of families have milk, but usually only in very small amounts ;
few eat meat, and little of that. So the energy value of the
food is inadequate, and animal protein is very low. We have
already seen that there is a marked incidence of gross vitamin
deficiency diseases. The complaint is sometimes made by
Europeans that "the natives" are idle and bad workers. The
food position is part of the explanation ; the next chapter
gives another part. In 1933 the Director-General of the
Indian Medical Service estimated that 40 per cent of Indian
villages had populations too high for the existing food supply.
Even when the weather is favourable periods of scarcity are
reckoned to occur for 20 per cent of villages in every ten years ;
but if the rains fail, there is famine. It is reckoned that India
needs 50 per cent more food than is now, in 1949, available, to
feed its present population adequately. The experiments
described on page 104 illustrate the effect that a better diet
can have on the health and physique of Indians.

On *China* we have less information, but what there is suggests
a situation similar to that in India. Again there is little
consumption of meat or of dairy products. There is much
severe deficiency of the B vitamins and of vitamin A. The
famines of China are as notorious as those of India and may
well have killed more people (100m. has been suggested),
during the past hundred years ; but China has lacked a government capable of collecting accurate figures about them.

Absence of statistics cannot be complained of if we turn to
the British colonies in *Africa*. An extensive survey, published
by the Colonial Office in 1938, showed that in these vast areas
too the majority of the people suffer near-starvation on diets of
poor quality. The Africans for the most part in the past had
effective forms of agriculture or stock-raising, together with
appropriate tribal customs, which varied a great deal from
place to place. Much of this social organisation has been over-
thrown, and the Africans in many areas have been obliged by
economic pressure to leave villages to the women and children

and to work for the Europeans in plantations, mines and other establishments. The primitive agriculture has consequently been disrupted, but nothing satisfactory has replaced it.

So far we have considered colonial or semi-colonial peoples. But even in the agricultural lands of *south-eastern Europe*, in Rumania, Bulgaria, Yugoslavia and Hungary, diets were very bad, especially in winter. In Hungary even the energy-value of the peasants' food seems to have been deficient.

DIET IN THE WEST

It might be expected that, while the industrially backward countries had underfed populations, the relatively rich countries of the west would have no difficulty in getting an adequate supply of good food. An examination of the situation in England and the United States shows that this was far from true.

Until the beginning of the nineteenth century the problem in England was to produce enough food. Most people produced their own, and if the harvest was good all was well. This had been the position for centuries among the peasantry. Chaucer's widow in the *Nonnes Preestes Tale* did not have much variety :

> No winne dranke she, neyther white ne red :
> Hire bord was served most with white and black.
> Milk and broun bread, in which she found no lack,
> Seinde bacon, and sometime an ey or twey.

But a diet based on milk, rye or wholemeal bread, bacon and eggs is not likely to lead to serious deficiency, except perhaps of vitamin C. Little sugar was eaten, but there was a good supply of vegetables, at least in summer. A bad aspect of this state of affairs was that it led to occasional famines when crops failed.

Industrialism led to a great change. The industrialists wanted cheap food for the working people in the towns, since without it they could not get hands for the factories. The landowners, on whose estates food was produced, wanted food prices kept up. At the beginning of the nineteenth century there was a duty on imported wheat, and the 4-lb. loaf cost fourteen pence. Wages were one or two shillings a day. In 1846 the factory workers and industrialists achieved the repeal

of the Corn Laws : the import duty came off, and by 1900 the
4-lb. loaf cost sixpence. During the nineteenth century, as
we shall see in chapter 14, the population of England and
Wales doubled, and from being agricultural became predomin-
antly urban and industrial, living largely on cheap imported
cereal foods, sugar and potatoes. Wheat was eaten mainly as
white flour, and the annual consumption of sugar rose from a
few pounds per head to nearly one hundredweight. Agriculture
declined and the consumption of dairy products, vegetables,
fruit and oatmeal fell. Rickets and scurvy became common.
At the beginning of the century the minimum recruiting height
for the army was 5 feet 6 inches ; by the end it had had to be
reduced to 5 feet. It was the high proportion of recruits
rejected as unfit for service in the Boer war, at the turn of the
century, that eventually led to the introduction of school meals.

But it was not until the 1930's that knowledge of nutrition
made possible the setting up of dietary standards. Given a
standard it then became possible, by investigation of the diets
of large numbers of families, to determine the extent and
character of the still prevailing malnutrition. It must be
admitted that standards vary, and that there is even now no
final agreement on the necessary amounts of certain essentials :
we know that nobody can do without vitamin C, for instance,
but we cannot lay down precisely, with reasonable certainty, the
minimum any person, or even any class of persons, must have in
order to avoid all ill effects. It is easy to see the effects of gross
deficiencies, but far from easy to relate less obvious symptoms,
such as an apparently excessive susceptibility to some infections,
to shortage of a particular vitamin. One difficulty is that
individuals almost certainly vary genetically in their vitamin
needs. Tooth decay is unquestionably influenced by diet ; but
one child may have excellent teeth, while another on the same
diet may have extensive decay. And complexities do not end
there. In one investigation it was found impossible to induce
certain volunteers to show signs of vitamin B_1 deficiency :
although deprived of the vitamin they continued to excrete it
in their urine, and it seemed that they were synthesising it in
their bodies. Further experiments gave the explanation. A
drug was fed to them in sufficient amounts to kill most of the

bacteria in their intestines. (Our intestines always contain harmless bacteria.) When this had been done the excretion of B_1 stopped : it was the bacteria which had been producing it. Thus our liability to vitamin B_1 deficiency depends in part on the bacteria we harbour.

Despite these difficulties nutrition surveys have given valuable information. Those carried out before the war illustrate the state of nutrition attained in a period of relative stability. The relationship between income and nutritional level was clearly shown in Orr's famous report "Food, health and income", published in 1935. The figures on page 193 show that, on the standard chosen, the food of at least half of the population of England and Wales was seriously deficient. The malnourished 50 per cent. belonged to the lower income groups, and since the poorer people had, on the average, larger families than those better off it was reckoned that about 75 per cent of the children of England and Wales were inadequately fed. Later surveys confirmed Orr's general findings. Within each income group there is wide variation from the average : some individuals or families do very much better, and others correspondingly worse. This individual variation has been very clearly shown in American work. But this does not invalidate the conclusions drawn from the surveys.

Orr's results, and those of later workers, show what, in fact, people do eat. If every housewife were a skilled dietician, had unlimited time and patience, access to the cheapest markets, and adequate skill and cooking facilities, the nutritional level would doubtless be higher. This however is an academic point, except that it suggests the need for a long-term policy of education and of improvement in kitchen equipment. However, the malnutrition of the poor cannot be attributed to ignorance : Orr's figures showed that, even with the maximum of knowledge and skill, 20 per cent of the population, with then existing wages and prices, could not have afforded a satisfactory diet. His comment was as follows :

It has been suggested that the standard adopted, viz. what is needed to enable people to attain their inherited capacity for health and physical fitness, is so high that it is impracticable. One writer terms it "utopian". In animal husbandry,

ESTIMATED   CONSUMPTION   PER   HEAD   OF   CERTAIN   FOODSTUFFS   BY

INCOME   GROUPS

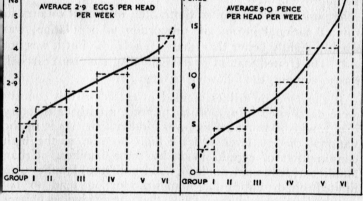

FOOD AND INCOME

Some of the graphs from Orr's survey of nutrition in England in 1935. They illustrate the relationship between income and nutrition, and help to account for the lower average height and inferior physique of the children of the poor. Group I is the poorest ten per cent, group IV the wealthiest ten per cent ; each other group represents 20 per cent of the population an optimum standard, far from being utopian, is regarded as good practice. Every intelligent stock farmer in rearing animals tries to get a minimum diet for maximum health and physical fitness. A suggestion that he should use a lower standard would be regarded as absurd. If children of the ' three lower groups were reared for profit like young farm stock, giving them a diet below the requirements for health would be financially unsound. Unfortunately, the health and physical fitness of the rising generation are not marketable commodities which can be assessed in terms of money.

England and Wales were not exceptional in their nutritional status among industrial countries. Germany, for instance, in the period immediately before 1933, was slightly worse. The Germans drank more milk, on the whole, than the English, but ate much less butter and less meat. The exceptional countries were four which produce food of animal origin for export : Australia, New Zealand, Holland and Denmark. In all these the nutritional level of the whole population (except the Australian aborigines) was high, and required relatively little improvement.

The position in the United States, the wealthiest country in terms of national income in proportion to population, was probably slightly better than that of England. But it was not good. The United States Department of Agriculture Yearbook for 1939 contains the following passage :

If the total quantities of food produced in this country were distributed in proportion to need, a fairly satisfactory diet would be provided for every individual. As it is, the national dietary level appears high because of the high consumption of certain foods by some families. Urban families with limited funds for food and rural families with limited opportunities for home production tend to lay emphasis on the kind of foods that satisfy obvious hunger cheaply and to neglect those that satisfy also the "hidden nutritional hungers"—for vitamins and minerals—described by science.

The point is put in another way elsewhere in the same volume, where it is calculated that to raise consumption of all groups to the level of the most favoured it would be necessary to increase the production of milk by 20 per cent, of butter by 15, tomatoes and citrus fruits 70, leafy and yellow vegetables 100 and eggs 35 per cent. The similarity to England holds too in the relationship between poverty and malnutrition. In 1936 about 32 per cent of families and single individuals in the U.S. had incomes under 750 dollars a year, and it was reckoned that none of these could afford satisfactory diets at the prices then prevailing.

THE EFFECTS OF BETTER FOOD

Conclusions of this sort were at first received with a good deal of scepticism, but they are confirmed, not only by the results of further surveys, but also by study of the effects of improving diets. The effects are most clearly seen in children and in women before and after childbirth. In a study of a village colony for boys some of the boys were allowed an extra ration of milk each day, while others remained on the usual diet. The average annual gain in weight of boys in the milk group was 6.98 lb. ; that of the boys receiving the normal diet, 3.85 lb. To quote Marrack :

> The experiment was kept going for three years, although many of the original boys left ; the milk group maintained their advantage throughout. What is perhaps more striking than these figures is the fact that the slowest-growing boys of the milk group grew faster than the fastest-growing boys of the basic group.
>
> Apart from the gain in weight and height, the boys who received the extra milk improved in their general condition. They lost the tendency to chilblains during the winter months, which was almost universal among the boys eating the basal diet ; their skins became softer and smoother ; they were more high spirited. A casual visitor entering the dining-hall would never fail to recognise the table at which the boys who received the extra ration of milk sat, as these boys were obviously more fit than the others. Furthermore, during the winter 1923-24 they were completely free from illness, although among the other boys the sickness rate had been somewhat higher than usual owing to influenza and a limited outbreak of measles and scarlet fever.

Other, similar experiments have since been done both in

Britain and the United States, with similar results. These results are paralleled in both countries by two well established facts : that the children of the poor are smaller, weaker and suffer more disease than those of the rich ; and that there has been a steady improvement during the twentieth century in all classes.

The clearest index of improvement is the increase in average weight and height of children of all ages. To quote Marrack again :

> In some thirty years the average height of a London school boy at any age from five to thirteen has increased by over two inches, and the average weight by from 5 lb. at five years to 11 lb. at twelve years ; the weight of the older girls has increased by over 13 lb. This improvement has not been confined to London.

Thus the effects of the dietary collapse of the nineteenth century have been partly reversed in the twentieth. Similar changes have been observed both in Canada and the United States.

The improvement cannot be attributed wholly to better nutrition. We shall see in the next chapter that the amount of infectious disease has been much reduced, and this is only partly due to better food and consequent higher resistance. Smaller families and child-welfare clinics have both led to better care of children. A number of other changes may have contributed. Nevertheless we need not doubt that food has played a major part. We shall see below that even during the second world war the improvement continued.

Growth in height and weight is generally used in assessing physical condition. This is primarily because both height and weight can be measured accurately and quickly. However, it is further justified by the fact that other qualities vary with physical growth. Children who grow most rapidly also, on the average, have higher resistance to infection and are better at all kinds of school activity, both physical and intellectual. This does not signify that small people are inferior, but only that, on the whole, growth in the ordinary sense goes with the growth of intellect and ability.

When we come to study the effect of diet on pregnant women the simplest criteria to use are the proportion of deaths in childbirth, stillbirths, and deaths of the children in the first month of life. This has been done in several investigations in Britain and Canada. In one, carried out in South Wales in 1934, when there was much unemployment among the miners, over 27,000 women were studied, some of whom were given extra food. Here are figures obtained in one year.

		Attended clinic only	Clinic + food
Maternal death rate	⎫	11.29	4.77
	⎬ per 1,000 live births		
Stillbirth rate + neonatal mortality	⎭	84.0	59.0

The extra food included a small amount of protein, together with calcium, phosphorus, iron, vitamin A, and B vitamins. This supplement, although it markedly influenced death rates, still left the total diet of the women far below any recommended standard.

To sum up the two preceding sections we may quote the *World Food Survey* published by the Food and Agriculture Organisation in 1946 :

Calculations based on the prewar populations of the individual countries show that in the years before the war—

In areas containing over half the world's population food supplies at the retail level (not actual intake) were sufficient to furnish an average of less than 2,250 calories per caput daily.

Food supplies furnishing an average of more than 2,750 calories per caput daily were available in areas containing somewhat less than a third of the world's population. The remaining areas, containing about one-sixth of the world's population, had food supplies that were between these high and low levels. . . .

The high-calorie areas include most of the western world, all of North America, and much of Europe. Oceania and the Union of Socialist Soviet Republics also belong to this group, but it includes only three countries in South America.

The medium-calorie areas include most of Asia, a part of the Middle East, all of Central America, and probably parts of South America and Africa which were not covered by this survey.

But averages do not tell the whole story. They conceal many sharp differences. Whatever the average calorie intake

14

of a country, some people obtain considerably more than the average while a large number have less. Even in the countries with the most liberal food supplies and the highest calorie intake, it is well known that a considerable part of the population is not well nourished. There are wide local variations in food supply which are not brought out by average figures for the whole population.

Poverty is the chief cause of malnutrition. In the course of preparing this survey prewar calorie consumption was compared with national incomes per person as far as these are known. It is interesting to observe that all the countries in which the supply of calories per caput was less than 2250 a day were countries in which the average per caput income was less than U.S. $100 a year. At the other end of the scale there were 365 million people living in countries in which the average supply of calories exceeded 2900 a person a day. Of these, 342 million were in countries in which the average income exceeded U.S. $200 a person a year.

Thus for the world as a whole it can be said, "Tell me what you earn and I will tell you how you eat." There are exceptions, but in general well-to-do countries fare well nutritionally, poor countries fare badly, and the poorest groups within these countries fare the worst.

Food Distribution

The F.A.O., in the same publication, gives a table showing world food needs in 1960. The figures in this table are the percentage increases in the production of the various types of food, required to raise nutrition throughout the world to a fairly satisfactory level. They are calculated on the assumption of a 25 per cent increase in world population. Here are the figures :

Commodity	Increase per cent
Cereals	21
Roots and tubers	27
Sugar	12
Fats	34
Pulses	80
Fruit and vegetables	163
Meat	46
Milk	100

There is, in 1949, no evidence that even half these increases will have been achieved by 1960. The only thing on which we can congratulate ourselves is that, for the first time, the world's food needs have at least been roughly assessed.

Feeding people well depends not only on production but also on satisfactory methods of distribution. The first country to attempt the planned production and distribution of food in peace time was the Soviet Union. The problem was mainly one of a peasant population with adequate cereals except in times of famine, but inadequate meat, vegetables and dairy produce. Farms were too small for economic production, and methods of cultivation were primitive. The total area under cultivation also was too small. By 1939 75 per cent of agricultural land was in the hands of co-operatives (described in the previous chapter) and much of the remainder consisted of state farms. The cultivated area has been much increased, and the extra land used for growing vegetables and animal food. From 1933 livestock greatly increased : cattle, in particular, by 646 per cent in five years. By 1935 it was possible to abolish rationing, and in 1947 it has again been found unnecessary, but food distribution remains planned. A League of Nations report, published in 1936, referred especially to the development of communal restaurants and factory canteens ; even the collective farms had mobile kitchens bringing meals to the workers in the fields. Special attention was given to the diet of children, and in particular to the supply of free meals in schools. This probably accounts for the rapid increase in children's height and weight observed after the revolution. In Leningrad, as early as the period 1925-32, the 13-year averages for boys increased by 3 inches and 11 pounds respectively, and for girls by 1.5 inches and 9 pounds.

The Soviet Union provides an instance of planning for a vast agricultural country with a population which was initially largely illiterate. The soviet experience has therefore much to tell us of the possibilities for the other great peasant and backward areas. On the other hand the experience of the United Kingdom during the second world war shows what can be done in a densely populated industrial country. Despite the lowered food imports, which were not fully balanced by increased home production, the nutritional level for the country as a whole was raised. In 1943, for instance, although average fat consumption had fallen, protein consumption had increased ; and in both vitamins and minerals there had been improvement, although the adequacy of the amounts of vitamins A, B_1 and B_2, and C was doubtful. The improvement depended on three things: the rationing of most essential foods at controlled prices ; the availability of adequate energy food in the form of unrationed bread and potatoes, also at controlled prices ; and full employment and consequently higher incomes for the poor. (For a time after the war, however, both bread and potatoes had to be rationed, though at a high level.) Both agricultural production at home, and the import of foods, were determined largely by the known nutritional needs of the population. There were several similarities to the Russian scheme, including the organisation of communal meals at low prices ; special supplements for children and mothers ; and extra rations for some classes of workers. It was also recognised that rationing and other measures would be less effective if people did not understand them, or made wrong use of the foods available. Attempts were therefore made to improve public knowledge of food values. Habits had to be changed : such valuable foods as dried egg and dried milk were unfamiliar ; many people were unaccustomed to eating cheese, which was one of the most valuable of the rationed foods; and campaigns had to be run to induce mothers to make use of the vitamin supplements supplied for their children and themselves.

These two examples illustrate the complex of biochemical, economic and social problems involved in making a national food policy. Despite the complexity it is now possible to define with precision all the main steps to be taken to feed any given community. This in itself is an enormous advance. At present, if we survey the whole world, the knowledge is being applied only piecemeal, and indeed can be only so applied in many countries until food production is increased. Nevertheless, provided that man applies himself to peaceful ends during the rest of the twentieth century he can reasonably look forward to a well-fed world at the end of it : the result will be an unprecedented state of health and well-being for every nation.

CHAPTER 13

DEATH

Death be not proud, though some have called thee
Mighty and dreadfull ; for, thou art not soe.
JOHN DONNE

THROUGHOUT human history the two great causes of premature
death have been famine and infectious disease. The casualties
due directly to war have been trifling by comparison, at least
until the middle of the twentieth century. The conquest of
infection remains second only to feeding people, among the
twentieth century objectives of applied science.

The problem arises from the crowded populations of civilisation. Primitive peoples untouched by advanced cultures seem
to have few epidemic or endemic infections, though individuals
rarely reach more than middle age. This is inferred from study
of their skeletons, and from the reports of the civilised men
who first reach them. Once regular contact with advanced
communities is established there is a complete change : since
primitive groups have not before been exposed to the disease-
causing microbes of civilisation they are highly susceptible to
them ; this is at least partly because the first experience they
have of them is a sudden, heavy infection : there is little
possibility of getting a mild or undetectable attack from a light
infection, such as often occurs in most communities. It is
also probable that isolated groups, not having been selected for
resistance to these diseases, are genetically more susceptible
than larger communities. Thus the inhabitants of Tierra de
Fuego, in less than a century, were reduced in numbers from
about 60,000 to 200, largely through infection with smallpox,
measles and tuberculosis.

These three diseases are mainly airborne, and so depend
for their spread directly on the crowding of people together.
But the density of civilised populations also gives opportunities
for other noxious organisms. Water supplies may be infected ;
sewage and other household waste may harbour the germs of

disease or the animals that carry them ; food itself, in its journey from the farm to the consumer, may become infected, and is liable, like waste, to maintain populations of germ-bearing pests such as flies and rats, as well as the human population for which it is intended.

THE "SANITARY IDEA"

None of this was properly understood anywhere until the middle of the nineteenth century, when the germ theory of disease was established. Although a relationship between disease and filth had long been suspected, the connexion was not proved. It was believed that "foul airs" or miasmas were the agents of disease, and the name of *malaria* (bad air) remains a memorial to this view. Microscopists had demonstrated the presence of bacteria and other microbes in a variety of places, including decaying material, but it was thought that these organisms grew directly from the stuff they lived on. The foundation of bacteriology was the demonstration that microbes do not appear "spontaneously" in any medium, however suitable for their growth ; they appear only if the medium has been exposed to infection from elsewhere : microbes, like larger organisms, grow only from other, similar bodies. Thus it came to be realised that filth caused disease on account of microbes which grow in it and which can also live in men's bodies.

Infection from these sources is far from being the cause of all disease. (In the last chapter we had examples of deficiency diseases which are in no way infectious ; and in chapter 3 we referred to abnormal conditions which are fixed genetically, and are independent of environmental effects.) Moreover, most microbes are harmless. But many of the worst killers of children and of men and women in their prime turned out to be infections preventible by sanitary measures.

The need for these measures had never been so great as in the new industrial towns of the nineteenth century. The squalor and degradation of the working population in English towns is fully described in a series of official reports published during the 1840's. Chadwick, the inventor of the expression the "sanitary idea" wrote :

Such is the absence of civic economy is some of our towns
that their condition in respect to cleanliness is almost as bad
as that of an encamped horde, or an undisciplined soldiery.

He describes army standing orders for camp sanitation, and
goes on :

The towns whose populations never change their encamp-
ment have no such care, and whilst the houses, streets,
courts, lanes, and streams are polluted and rendered pesti-
lential, the civic officers have generally contented themselves
with the most barbarous expedients, or sit still amidst the
pollution, with the resignation of Turkish fatalists, under the
supposed destiny of the prevalent ignorance, sloth and filth.

Similarly the Frenchman, Blanqui, describes how in 1849, in
the industrial town of Lille, 3,000 families lived in unventilated,
insanitary cellars.

Improvement required the setting up of a national public
health organisation in each country, and effective public
health departments for each local government authority. This
was a big task, both administratively and technically. Engin-
eers, sanitary inspectors, dustmen and sewermen, as well as
doctors, had to be recruited, trained and paid. It is only
recently that, even in England, all houses in towns have had a
reliable piped water supply free from infection ; (the poorer
houses often have even now only one tap, and in the country
much water still comes from wells, some quite shallow and
easily infected) ; but today most urban areas have, not only
enough water for drinking, cooking, washing and cleaning, but
also a bacteriological service to keep watch on the quality of
the water supplied. A necessary complement to a good water
supply is an efficient system of drains and sewers. In 1840
household waste of all kinds was put in cesspools (Windsor
Castle had 250 of them), or human excrement was collected in
heaps for sale as manure ; refuse collection was unorganised
and sporadic, where it existed at all. The new working-class
houses whose occupiers suffered these conditions were flimsy,
airless, ill-lit and commonly built in terraces back-to-back, with
only a narrow alley in front. Some of these houses are still in
use.

Although the first attempts to improve the hygiene of cities were made even before the elements of bacteriology were understood, the squalor remained almost untouched for most of the century ; the efforts of the wealthy taxpayers who did not wish to spend money on the poor, of the water companies, of some sections of the medical profession and of other vested interests prevented progress for several decades. Nevertheless, by the first decade of the twentieth century the application of the sanitary idea had brought a vast change in mortality and morbidity from some major diseases, not only in England but also in the main countries of western Europe, and in the United States. The extent and limits of this advance can be shown if we consider the main epidemic diseases of human populations.

PESTILENCE

Throughout the world the worst *water-borne* diseases are cholera, typhoid and various forms of dysentery. Today cholera is called a "tropical disease", but there were four major outbreaks in western Europe during the nineteenth century. Epidemics are nearly always due to infection of drinking water ; in one famous instance a single infected well near Piccadilly Circus, in London, caused 485 deaths in ten days. Cholera is no longer a disease of western Europe, but as this chapter is being written a serious epidemic is reported in Egypt, and it is continually present in the densely populated tropical lands. Much the same applies to typhoid fever, or more generally to the enteric fevers of which typhoid is the worst, but they have not so completely disappeared from the western world. One of the most notorious epidemics was in Plymouth, Pennsylvania, in 1885. About 1,200 persons in a population of 8,000 had typhoid in the spring of that year, and one in ten died. During the winter a man living near a stream that flowed into the town's reservoir had had typhoid, and each night his wife had thrown his excreta on to the frozen ground. When the thaw came in the spring the accumulation was washed into the brook and infected the reservoir. The last serious epidemic in Britain, at Croydon in 1937, was similarly traced to the individual who was the source of the infection. He was one of a party of men working on an unchlorinated well, who had been in the habit of urinating nearby ; the man had

	1871-80	1901-10	1921-30	1938	1941
SMALLPOX					
TYPHUS					
ENTERIC FEVER					
MEASLES					
WHOOPING COUGH					
DIPHTHERIA					
INFLUENZA					
CEREBRO SPINAL FEVER					

MORTALITY

Deaths from eight diseases, per 100,000 persons, in England and Wales. The first group of diseases has been almost wiped out, and the second has become much less serious. The third represents some new problems that have arisen in the twentieth-century had typhoid and was a carrier. There were 311 cases, with 42 deaths. A century earlier such an incident would have attracted little attention, but in 1937 it aroused great public interest for many weeks, and was the subject of an official enquiry. In this case the public health organisation had failed at two points : the well had been unchlorinated, and a healthy typhoid carrier had not been detected by bacteriological tests and prevented from working where he might infect the water supply.

The diseases carried by water may also be *food-borne*, and food can be a source of other infections as well. There are several forms of "food-poisoning" caused by bacteria or other disease organisms, and gastro-enteritis is a general term for the condition caused by these infections. They are especially serious in infants and young babies. Cleanliness in the handling and preparation of food at all stages ; preventing infected persons from working in food establishments ; and the use of effective preserving methods for canned and bottled foods : these are the principal preventive measures. In general food-borne disease is less likely to cause epidemics on a large scale than is disease carried by water. Milk, however, occupies a special place among foods : it is distributed in bulk to very large numbers of people in towns, and it is as good a food for some bacteria as it is for men. Infected milk can cause epidemics of typhoid, dysentery, tonsilitis and undulant fever. Even worse, it is the source of one type of tuberculosis. The heat treatment, or pasteurisation, of milk, which is now compulsory in some advanced communities, can prevent the transmission of all these infections.

Food may be infected, not only by man himself, but by various *animals* : flies provide the most familiar example, and are still a menace in the western world as carriers of germs of enteritis and food poisoning.

But rat fleas, lice and mosquitoes take pride of place among animal carriers of disease. All these infect man directly and not through food or water. Rat fleas are the source of plague, the Black Death of the middle ages. The plague bacillus is primarily a parasite in the bodies of various species of wild rodents, varying from ground squirrels in central Asia to rabbits in California. In these animals it causes little harm, and it certainly does not give rise to epidemics with a high mortality. It is transmitted from one individual to another by fleas, and rats become infected in the same way. Rat populations too may maintain a comparatively mild plague infection. Human infection occurs where there are many infected rats, and the rats have comparatively large numbers of fleas. These conditions hold today in large parts of India and China, and there are plague reservoirs also in North and South Africa, and in North America. Thus plague in man is a by-product of a disease of rodents. We know for certain of three world outbreaks, or pandemics, of plague, though it is likely that others occurred before them. A pandemic begins suddenly, spreading over a large area, such as Europe, within a few years ; at this stage the proportion of the population getting plague is high—perhaps 10 per cent—and the *usually* mortality among those infected varies between about 50 and 100 *usually* per cent ; the highest mortality occurs if the bubonic form gives place to pneumonic plague, when the lungs are involved and bacilli are coughed into the air. For a century or more after the first outbreak plague continues intermittently and with diminishing intensity. Finally in large areas it disappears completely.

We cannot explain this sequence. The first fully authenticated pandemic, the "plague of Justinian", began in the sixth century, and we have no detailed knowledge of what happened. The second was the Black Death which began in the fourteenth century, and reached France and England in 1349. The initial mortality, though high, was probably less disastrous than the steady drain of lives and health that followed during the next hundred years. This was a period of falling population and collapsing economy in western Europe, and plague made a major contribution to that state of affairs. The last flare-up in England was the "great plague of London" of 1664. The third pandemic is still going on as this book is written. It began in China, probably in the 1870's, spread rapidly to India, and then to the main ports of Africa and Asia Minor. Europe largely escaped. England had a few cases during the period 1910-21, and rodents in an area in East Anglia were infected at that time.

Plague is far from being a simple problem of public health, and we cannot attribute Europe's escape simply to improved hygiene and precautions against rats at the ports, though they doubtless played some part. With our present knowledge the remedy for plague is prevention by killing rats, and by reducing filth that encourages them ; protection can also be given by inoculation. We have still to get full understanding of the complex biological relationships between the plague-ridden rodent populations, their fleas and ourselves.

While plague is a problem of the rats that live in our houses, and of public cleanliness, epidemic typhus fever is a problem of the lice that live on our bodies and of personal cleanliness. This, the worst form of typhus, has destroyed armies and altered the course of wars. The great outbreaks occur when unwashed people are crowded together, and the lice can move rapidly from one to another. In earlier times alternative names for typhus were jail fever and hospital fever. The habit of washing which has become so widespread in the western world in modern times has made perhaps a contribution to disease prevention comparable with the control of the water supply. A Lancashire miner, in 1842, was asked how often the coal-drawers washed their bodies. He is reported to have replied :

> None of the drawers ever wash their bodies. I never wash my body ; I let my shirt rub the dirt off. I wash my neck and ears and face, of course.

Even more to the point is the cheerful mention in the diary of Samuel Pepys, a First Lord of the Admiralty, of the presence of twenty lice in his hair one evening—"more than I have had this many a long day. And so with great content to bed."

The diseases so far discussed are called "tropical" in Britain, because they have been largely banished from the temperate zone. The main mosquito-borne infections have a more permanent claim to the name, since they are almost confined to the tropics and sub-tropics. It is true that malaria can occur as far north as Archangel, and that one form of it turned up regularly in the London hospitals as recently as the 1860's. But ague, as it was called, was never such a menace in the north as it has been, and still is, in hotter climates. In large parts of the most densely populated countries malaria is almost universal, and it is the world's leading cause of infectious illness and death. A conservative estimate of its total incidence suggests that a quarter of the world's population suffer from it. In India the number of people treated for malaria each year is of the order of ten million, but it is certain that this is only a small proportion of the total infected. Malaria differs from the acute infections (such as plague and typhus) in being, very often, a chronic disease. An acute disease either kills in a few days or weeks, or subsides ; a chronic infection may persist for years, and perhaps for a lifetime. People with chronic malaria are weak and lethargic, and the uninformed and uninfected European, seeing them, is led to believe that all "natives" are naturally lazy. We have seen that the effects of chronic under-nutrition may encourage him in this view.

The principal means of preventing endemic malaria is destruction of mosquitoes of the genus *Anopheles*. This is a formidable task requiring a large organisation of trained persons. Methods include the draining of marshes and streams, where the mosquitoes breed ; poisoning the water ; and the introduction of plants or fishes that prevent breeding. What is done depends partly on the species of Anopheles. Mosquito teams applying these methods have already had considerable success in countries as diverse as India, Italy, Panama and Brazil. In Central and South America, and in West Africa, they are called on to operate also against *Aëdes ægypti*, the mosquito that carries yellow fever. It was the destruction both of *Anopheles* and *Aëdes* that finally made possible the building of the Panama Canal.

All these diseases can be prevented, and in some places have been prevented, by the application of a rather wide inter-pretation of the sanitary idea. They represent the easiest targets for public health authorities. This is because they depend on other species besides ourselves, whereas most infectious diseases are carried from man to man. This is the case with the group of *air-borne* infections, which are in principle at least a more difficult problem. (It is true that diseases such as plague and typhus can be air-borne, but they are not so as a rule.) It is an extraordinary fact that the worst of them, smallpox, had been shown to be preventible more than half a century before the germ theory of disease was established, since the technique of vaccination was invented before the end of the eighteenth century. At that time few people in Europe escaped having smallpox at some time in their lives, and about one in twelve of infected persons died. Most survivors were disfigured for life by the pockmarks, and some were blinded. Today deaths from smallpox are rare in the west, partly as a result of vaccination.

YEAR	PERCENTAGE OF CHILDREN IMMUNISED	CASES	DEATHS
1935-9 (Average)	UNDER 5 PER CENT	59,314	2,875
1940	8 PER CENT	46,281	2,480
1941	30 PER CENT	50,797	2,600
1942	50 PER CENT	41,404	1,827
1943	55 PER CENT	34,662	1,371
1944	55 PER CENT	29,949	934
1945	58 PER CENT	25,246	722
1946	ABOUT 60 PER CENT	18,284	444

DIPHTHERIA IN ENGLAND AND WALES

Widespread immunisation of one-year-old children has gone far to defeat this disease

The other outstanding success against air-borne infection is that of immunisation against diphtheria : in the countries where it has been carried out on a majority of children it has been reduced to an almost negligible danger. In England and Wales at the beginning of the century 65 in every 100,000 children under 15 died of diphtheria. Between the wars, when the numbers of children immunised were relatively low, the figure was steady at about 29. During the 1940's the proportion of children immunised was greatly increased as a result of publicity campaigns by the government and local health authorities, and in 1947 the death-rate was down to 2 per 100,000. Even this could be improved on, given a sustained effort to get every child immunised at the age of one year.

The almost complete disappearance of diseases such as typhus, typhoid and smallpox in some countries is a triumph of applied science. It has involved the use not only of biological science, but also of engineering, chemistry and other disciplines. This knowledge is applicable, not only in the areas with good public health services, most of which are in the temperate zone, but also in the tropical lands, with their immense populations, where the great epidemic diseases remain as potent as ever. There is a notion that the tropics must be unhealthy, both to people unaccustomed to them and also to the native inhabitants, but there is no valid evidence to support this view. The temperate zone also was "unhealthy" until public health measures brought improvement. The "white man's grave" of West Africa was so called for reasons that need no longer apply today : in particular it is a home of malaria, which is now preventible. Certain diseases occur mainly or solely in hot countries, just as others, such as rickets, belong mainly to the lands in which there is little sunlight for part of the year. Perhaps, if the Africans had colonised large areas of the temperate zone, northern Europe would have been called "the black man's grave", although it is in fact possible for Africans to live there in good health.

The tropical countries remain graveyards by comparison with advanced countries, at least for their native inhabitants, mainly because the known principles of public health have not yet been generally applied in them. Throughout the tropics the vitality of the people is sapped, not only by malaria and other diseases already mentioned, but by many others, of which hookworm is probably the most widespread. There are two types of hookworm : both are passed out of the bowel with the fæces, and re-enter a human being through the skin. The people who get it in large numbers are those who live in communities with inadequate sanitation and who do not wear shoes. Hookworm is rarely fatal, but it is chronically enfeebling. We do not know how many millions of people are infected with hookworm, but we do know that there are whole communities, for instance in the West Indies, living a depressed existence on account of it.

No full and accurate account of death and sickness in these backward areas can yet be given. "Some sixteen hundred million people", says Sorsby, "inhabit these zones, and the extent of morbidity and mortality can be assessed only approximately."

It is appalling even in such relatively highly organised countries as British India. The total mortality is over twice that for England and Wales (in 1937, 22.4 per 1,000 against 9.3), infantile mortality is nearly three times as high (161.7 per 1,000 births against 58), and maternal mortality is exceptionally heavy. About 60 per cent of all deaths are attributed to 'fever', malaria being probably the largest single factor. Cholera, smallpox, plague, and dysentery—all conditions that reflect primitive sanitation—exacted a toll of nearly half a million lives in 1937, a fairly typical year. It is estimated that though only ten million Indians are treated for malaria, at least ten times that number are affected ; a conservative estimate gives the number of cases of leprosy at one million. The country is infested with lethal affections, the control of which presents no difficulty to medicine—but a high standard of living and vast sanitary schemes are essential. The mortality and morbidity in tropical countries is not 'racial' but environmental ; wherever planned reforms are carried through improvement follows.

The social character of much mortality and morbidity among subject races is illustrated by evidence from the U.S.A. and its possessions. In Ohio the mortality rate per 1,000 for the native white male population in 1930 was 10.4 and 20.2 for negro males (the corresponding female rates were 8.5 and 18.3) ; in the Philippines there was a marked difference in the white and native rates : in Manila in 1919-20 the rates for Americans and Filipinoes were 11.8 and 27.4 respectively ; in Hawaii, where the Japanese have a social status similar to that of the white population, the rates were 13.9 and 12.4 for these two sections against 39.5 for the indigenous poor population.

RESISTANCE

The great epidemic diseases can be avoided by rather simple and easily understood methods designed to block the routes by which the disease germs enter the body. For public health purposes the question is : are people liable to be infected, say, with the cholera germ ? If so, we must expect them to get cholera; if not, all is well. But, in general, infectious disease is not merely a result of the entry of a disease germ into the body : the body itself must be susceptible to the germ, or in other words, its resistance must be inadequate. It is a familiar fact that one attack of a particular disease may confer immunity, at least for a time. The immunity is a result of a change in the composition of the blood, and in some instances such a change can be induced by "inoculation" which gives rise to little or no discomfort. But the problem of resistance is far wider than this : we have already seen that *nutrition* is an important factor ; the *mental state* of a person may affect his resistance to some infections ; and a number of other environmental factors, including *housing* and, in some trades, *working conditions*, may be of vital importance.

All these effects can be illustrated from one disease, tuberculosis. In each year nearly 2,000 English and Welsh children die of tuberculosis, but the worst sufferers are young adults : about 1 in 20 of all deaths in England and Wales are due to tubercle, and the majority occur between the ages of 15 and 45 ; in a quarter of all cases the disease is first diagnosed between 15 and 25. In most European countries after the second world war (just as after the first) the position is far worse than in England. Even in the United States tuberculosis is third on the list of causes of death, coming after diseases of heart and blood vessels, and cancer. Apart from the principal diseases of infancy and childhood tubercle has a special importance compared with the other main causes of death : it kills people in their prime, whereas cancer and the disorders of the vascular system, scourges though they are, are largely problems of the later years of life.

TB - disease a product of economic circumstance

213

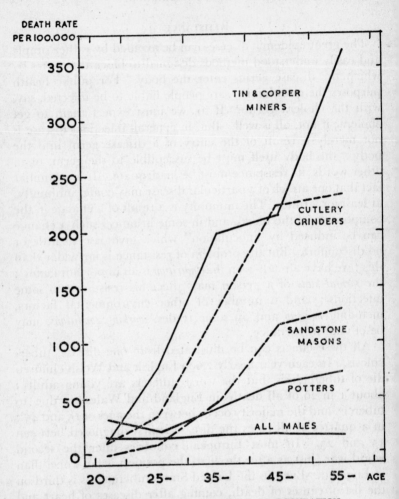

DEATH RATE
PER 100.000

350

300 — TIN & COPPER
MINERS

250

200 — CUTLERY
GRINDERS

150

100 — SANDSTONE
MASONS

50 — POTTERS

ALL MALES

0

20 —   25 —   35 —   45 —   55 — AGE

TUBERCULOSIS : THE INFLUENCE OF OCCUPATION

Work in certain trades greatly increases the likelihood of developing tuberculosis, and the longer a person remains in these trades, the greater the danger

In chapter 2 we saw that there is genetical variation in the liability to tuberculosis, but that there are several environmental factors which have a far more important influence in practice. Of these, working conditions that promote the development of tubercle are notorious : miners and others working where there is much silica dust in the air are especially liable to the disease, and prevention takes the form of various measures to reduce the amount of dust. There is also ample evidence that poor ventilation, in factories for example, increases the amount of tuberculosis. The same applies in the

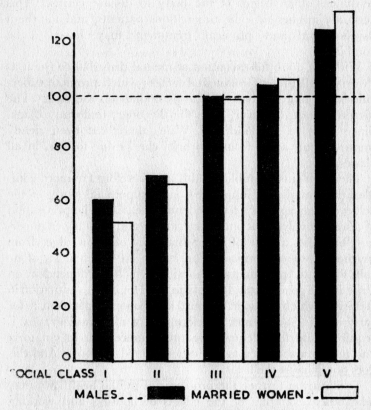

TUBERCULOSIS : THE INFLUENCE OF INCOME

Standardised mortality ratios at ages 20-65. Class 5, the poorest, come off worst home, but overcrowding there is also likely to cause a greater amount of air-borne infection from one member of a family to another. The connexion between nutritional deficiency and resistance to tubercle has not been fully worked out, but it is possible that vitamin C deficiency is important. As for mental state, it is well enough known that some illness, not caused by germs, such as gastric ulcer, is associated with anxiety and suppressed emotional tension (acting in a susceptible person), and that mental upset can cause symptoms of illness in any part of the body. Sometimes the effect is to reduce the resistance of an organ of the body to disease germs. This certainly applies to some tuberculosis patients, and for them psychological and physical treatment may have to be combined.

With the doubtful exception of mental disturbance (such as "worry") all the environmental factors which promote tuberculosis act more heavily on the poor than on the rich. The picture is not, however, even for the poor, uniformly black. Since 1875 in England and Wales there has been steady improvement, apart from two brief checks due to war, in all classes.

The problems of public health are therefore far more complex than might be supposed from a superficial study of the achievements against a few epidemic diseases. The prevention of disease involves not only bacteriology and sanitary engineering, but also a host of other branches of knowledge, from psychology to economics. The attack on tuberculosis alone calls for better nutrition and housing (which are dependent on a rise in the general standard of life), and for better ventilation in factories, which is again in part an economic problem ; for early diagnosis a greater development of mass radiography is required, and for adequate treatment more beds in sanatoria and more nurses, doctors and other trained persons. And this does not exhaust the list.

To illustrate further the problems of public health we may take other examples of the effects of housing and working conditions. An outstanding example is measles. If the population of England and Wales is divided into five groups, according to income level, it is found that the proportion of children who contract measles is roughly the same in each group ; but the proportion of children *dying* from measles in the lowest group is 19 times that of the highest. Whooping cough— which is the main killer of children between 1 and 5 years— shows a similar contrast. The difference between the social classes is, for these two diseases, entirely due to the bad housing of the poor and the difficulties that go with it : it has been shown, perhaps surprisingly, that nutrition does not affect it. Crowding makes it more likely that very young babies will get these diseases ; resistance is lower in the first year of life than later, and so many babies are killed. We have no such scientific standard for housing as we have for nutrition, but we can say that housing which makes it impossible for a baby to be put to sleep apart from the rest of the family is inadequate.

Another condition which has been proved to be affected by housing is rheumatic heart disease in children. In Britain it is probable that between one and five children in every 100 have rheumatic heart disease, and it is responsible for nearly all the deaths from heart disease before the age of 40. In one investigation a number of working class families were first classified by their economic position ; this is not the same as classifying them by total income, since a couple with one child and £5 a week are much better off than a family of seven with the same income. An arbitrary "poverty line" was then chosen, below which, it was assumed, a family could not maintain a standard of living adequate for health. Seventeen per cent of the families studied fell below this line, and among them the frequency of rheumatic heart disease was 39 per cent above the average. On the other hand, 22 per cent had at least double the chosen minimum income, and among them the frequency of the disease was 23 per cent below the average. One immediate conclusion could be drawn from these results : to get a satisfactory reduction in the rate of heart disease in children a standard of life well above the chosen minimum would be necessary. It is by objective standards such as this that minimum wages, family allowances and other factors influencing the standard of living, should be judged. Further analysis of the figures showed that the higher incidence of the disease among the poorest families was due mainly to over-

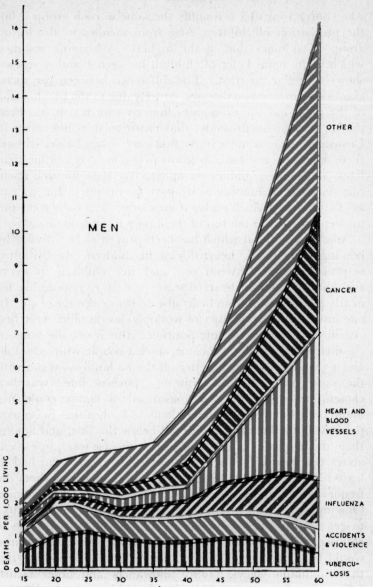

MORTALITY

The principal causes of death in England and Wales : men

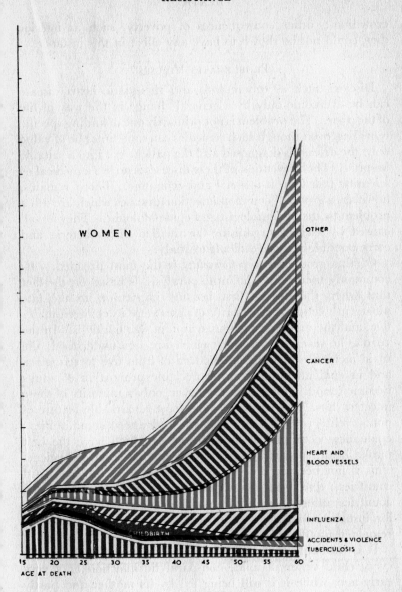

WOMEN

OTHER

CANCER

HEART AND
BLOOD VESSELS

INFLUENZA

CHILDBIRTH

ACCIDENTS & VIOLENCE
TUBERCULOSIS

15   20   25   30   35   40   45   50   55   60
AGE AT DEATH

MORTALITY

The principal causes of death in England and Wales : women

crowding : other consequences of poverty, such as inferior diet, could not be shown to have any effect in this instance.

PROBLEMATIC VIRUSES

Diseases such as tuberculosis and rheumatic heart disease can be overcome only by a general change in the way of life of the poor. The problem is not primarily one of finding specific remedies, even though such remedies can sometimes be of value once the disease is diagnosed and the patient got into a suitable hospital. The prevention of these diseases is no less a medical or scientific task than it is social and economic. There remains, however, a group of common infectious diseases which are still a problem to the bacteriologist and epidemiologist. They are all caused by viruses, organisms far smaller than bacteria and correspondingly more difficult to study.

Of this group acute *poliomyelitis* is the most dreaded. Its commonly used name, infantile paralysis, is based on the fact that when the disease first became important, in the late nineteenth century, a majority of cases were in children under five, and the most conspicuous symptom was paralysis. In the 1930's, however, for reasons which are not understood, the main incidence was among children of from five to ten years, and in epidemics today an appreciable proportion of adults become seriously infected ; moreover, only a minority of those infected show any paralysis. The most remarkable feature of poliomyelitis is that it is a disease of advanced communities : epidemics occur in just those countries which have the best public health organisations and the highest level of hygiene. This is not because the virus is not present in the backward countries : during the second world war soldiers from advanced countries suffered severely from poliomyelitis on being posted, for instance, to Asiatic countries. Yet the local inhabitants remained unaffected.

It is probable that in lands where hygiene is poor nearly every child suffers a mild, non-paralytic infection at a very early age, while it is still being fed by its mother and partly protected by substances in the milk, and that this sets up a natural resistance. In western countries, presumably, a proportion of children escape early infection, and so are susceptible, later on, to the acute form of the disease. Even then, it is believed, most of those infected show no serious symptoms : only a minority, in whom the virus invades a particular part of the nervous system, show any paralysis. In Britain more than 50 per cent of adults contain substances in their blood which indicate a previous infection by the virus, though they give no record of the actual disease.

The great problems are, how the infection is spread, and how to prevent it. It is known that the virus is passed out with the fæces : there are detectable amounts of the virus in the sewage of a city during an epidemic, though not at other times. This suggests the desirability of ordinary hygienic precautions. But it is almost certain that the virus is also air-borne ; it follows that crowds, especially in badly ventilated places, are to be avoided—another commonplace principle. There is evidence that fatigue increases the likelihood of severe infection, and so parents are recommended to avoid over-tiredness in their children during epidemics. Finally, it is fully established that the operation of removing the tonsils greatly increases the danger of infection, and as far as possible surgeons avoid carrying it out if there is a poliomyelitis epidemic. None of these precautions can prevent epidemics, and no further preventive measure is yet in sight.

The other virus diseases to be mentioned here are so commonplace as to be quite unfrightening ; yet they cause far more ill health and inconvenience, even suffering, than poliomyelitis. They include the common cold, a number of more severe infections without a definite name, and epidemic influenza. In one investigation of the work of general medical practitioners it was found that about one-third of all ailments treated in patients over sixteen belonged to this group. All are primarily due to infection with viruses, but how many different viruses are involved, and what decides the degree of illness in each infected person, are still unsolved problems.

Colds themselves may be due to more than one microbe, but research has been hampered by the fact that the common laboratory animals do not get colds ; chimpanzees do, but they are very expensive to keep : today research is done on human volunteers. In the United States the average number of colds a year for an adult is about 2.5, most of them in the colder half of the year. During each winter there are epidemic periods when the incidence of colds is particularly high. The susceptibility of individuals to colds varies very greatly and, what is less well known, any one person may vary a great deal from year to year in his liability to catch colds. There is good evidence that psychological state is an important factor in a person's response to infection, and this may be the explanation for the apparently favourable effect of some anti-cold vaccines : none of the vaccines so far used has proved effective under rigorous test. It is probable that low temperatures are not important in causing colds, but that variation of temperature is : in one experiment a group of medical students were kept for a fortnight in conditions of constant temperature and humidity ; every effort was made to give them colds by contact with infected persons or material, but all failed.

Rather more serious than colds is the group of infections commonly called influenza but different in character from true epidemic influenza. There is no accepted name for this group : the U.S. army name is curd (common undifferentiated respiratory disease), but the U.S. navy talks of cat fever (acute catarrhal fever). Some of these fevers may be due to the same viruses as colds, others to one of the true influenza viruses, but it appears to be certain that most are due to neither. It has been suggested that some are due to mild infection with the poliomyelitis virus.

Finally we come to *epidemic influenza*. This differs from colds and curd in producing mainly general toxic symptoms, such as headache and muscular pains ; there is less local effect on the nose, and less coughing. In a typical epidemic from 10 to 20 per cent of the population in a particular area develop the disease during a period of four to six weeks. Deaths due to influenza are confined to infants and old people. There are two viruses involved, called A and B, but epidemics due to virus B are relatively rare. Serious outbreaks of influenza A occur at intervals of two to four years : an epidemic seems to confer general immunity on a population for at least the following winter, sometimes for longer. What happens to the virus between epidemics is unknown, but it is possible that a few people can remain carriers for many months. There is no specific treatment for influenza.

In 1918-19 there was a unique pandemic, or world epidemic, of influenza, which is generally supposed to have been due to virus A although no direct evidence exists on this point. The most remarkable feature of the outbreak was the high mortality, especially among young adults. There is no explanation for the pandemic, and no reason to expect that it will ever be repeated.

All these diseases are transmitted through the air, probably by "droplet infection" in which the fine spray given out with each cough or sneeze is the main source of infection. Research on air sprays which might kill the viruses in crowded buildings and vehicles promises to give useful results. Dust particles may play a part in spreading infection, and the application of a light mineral oil, spindle oil, to the floors of public buildings reduces the amount of dust in the air and may have a preventive effect.

A potentially important line of study is provided by the very difficult problem of immunity to these diseases. It is a general rule that newcomers to an established community, for instance recruits entering an army camp, show a much higher incidence of respiratory disease than those who have been there six months or more. Similarly, isolated groups, such as the crews of ships exploring remote waters, or small island communities, may be quite free from colds, curd and influenza, yet show an explosive epidemic as soon as contact with members of other communities is made. It seems likely that in most groups there is a constant interchange of the local viruses and a consequent setting up of a temporary immunity ; so long as this immunity is regularly reinforced by repeated infection there will be freedom from the various diseases the viruses may cause. This does not however account for the fact that people do get respiratory diseases : no doubt the factors involved in the failure of immunity include the appearance of a new strain of virus in the neighbourhood, and a lowering of resistance in particular individuals.

True influenza confers a high degree of immunity to the virus which caused it, but this lasts only two or three months.

Vaccines which confer a similar immunity artificially have
already been made, and it is possible that they will soon be
of practical use. Whether we can hope that they will finally
prevent influenza epidemics altogether, as diphtheria immunisation can prevent diphtheria, is uncertain.

The story of these virus infections is therefore incomplete
and unsatisfying. It would have been easier to omit it
altogether, and to have restricted this chapter to the diseases of
which the scientific account is fairly complete. But to do so
would have been misleading : although the most obviously
urgent need in the field of public health is the application of
existing knowledge, especially in the backward lands, there is
still work for the research bacteriologist. The public are called
upon to support this research in various ways, notably by
paying for it, and they need to know something of the problems
which face the scientists.

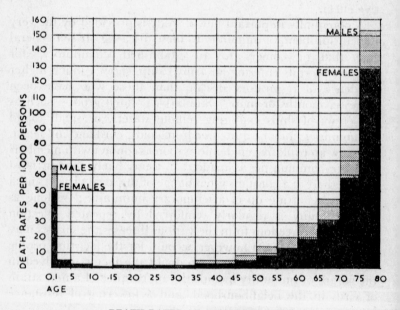

DEATH-RATES AT DIFFERENT AGES

The dangerous ages in the western world today are the first year
and after 60

HEALTH IS PURCHASABLE

The special health problems of the advanced countries can be studied from another point of view. Today, in the west, most people die either when they are very young, or over fifty : the great reduction in mortality has most affected the intermediate ages. This is why diseases which occur mainly in elderly people, in particular cancer and disorders of the heart and blood vessels, now loom so large in medical practice ; the proportion of men and women over fifty is far higher than ever before. The study of the problems of ageing, or gerontology, is only in its earliest stages, and little can usefully be said about it here. There is however much to be said about the health of children in their earliest years—a contemporary problem which deserves just as much attention.

We have seen that the health and physical and mental development of each individual is strongly influenced by the economic position of his parents. Nutritional level depends, in most countries, largely on income ; and nutrition affects, not only growth directly, but also susceptibility to many diseases. At the same time poverty involves bad housing, and so evokes a further group of diseases.

The combined effects of the various consequences of poverty in the advanced countries are clearly shown in the figures for diseases of children. The figure opposite shows that of all ages below 70 the first year of life has the highest death rate. The death rate in the first year is called the infant mortality, or IM. It does not include stillbirths. The IM for England and Wales in 1938 was 53, signifying that 53 infants died out of every 1,000 born alive. For the whole world this was rather low. The highest accurately recorded was that of Malta, where it was 243 in 1937 ; during the decade immediately before the second world war almost one in every four Maltese babies died in the first year of life. (Since then the Maltese IM has been reduced to about 116.) The highest figure for a large country was 241 for Chile ; the lowest, 31, was for New Zealand, though the Maori section of the population was less well off than the whites in this respect. In Europe, Iceland with 33 and Holland with 38 did best, and Roumania with 178 had the highest figure.

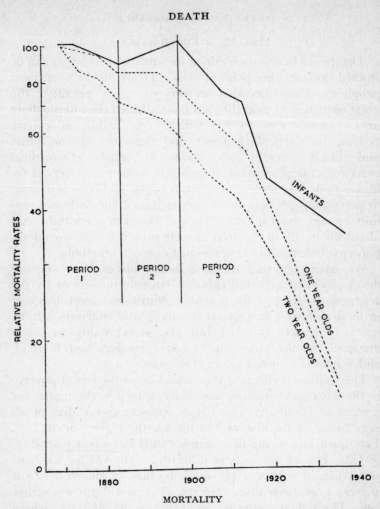

Changes in infant mortality in England and Wales, compared with death-rates at ages 1-2 and 2-3. Infant mortality lags behind in reduction

Until about 1900 the IM of England and Wales was much like that of Roumania or India today, but in the first forty years of the twentieth century it fell by about 66 per cent. However, there remains, even within Britain, much variation in IM between different towns. A few small towns have an

226

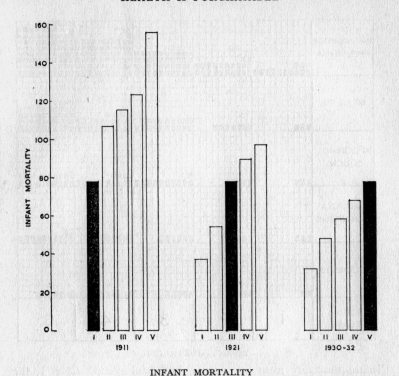

INFANT MORTALITY

Infant mortality by social class of father in England and Wales
Class 1 is highest income group

IM of less than 30, while in some larger ones, such as Liverpool
and Edinburgh, it approaches 100. This difference between
different places has been shown to be quite independent of
latitude : the fact that the south of England does better than
the north is evidently not because it is warmer or drier, but
because a smaller proportion of the inhabitants are in the
lower income groups. The figure above illustrates the
difference between the economic classes : the child of an
unskilled labourer is more than twice as likely to die in the
first year, as the child of a professional man. In later years
the differences between the classes become still greater ; no
doubt this is because the inferior environment of the poor has
a cumulative effect on the health of the growing child.

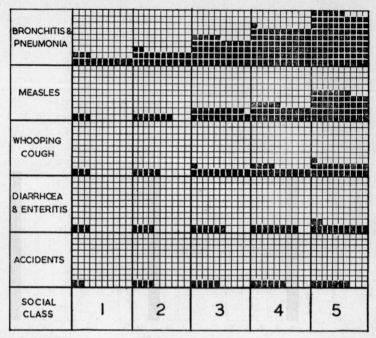

INFANT MORTALITY

Infant mortality from five causes, by social group. Class I, the "professional and managerial" group, is the wealthiest; class 5, the poorest

It has been claimed that improvement in the survival rate of working-class children is undesirable because large numbers of the "unfit"—of weaklings—are consequently kept alive ; there are then many who are unable to make an adequate contribution to maintaining themselves as useful members of society. This view is held in particular by those who believe the working-class to be genetically inferior. If this belief were true a fall in IM would be followed by a corresponding rise in mortality at later ages : relatively many of the weaklings would show their unfitness by dying before they reached old age. But no such effect is found. A lowered IM is always accompanied by lowered mortality in later years. Moreover, as death rates fall, so do sickness rates : that is indeed one reason why death rates are so much studied, since they provide a convenient index of health in general. Further evidence against the genetic inferiority of the poor is the fact that *congenital* malformations causing death in infancy are of roughly equal frequency in all classes ; and these conditions are largely of genetic origin and little affected by environment.

The improvement in IM in the western countries un-doubtedly reflects the better nutrition, housing, sanitation and medical care. It is shown in all classes, and it might be thought that differences between the different economic levels are of secondary importance. After all, the IM of the lowest income group in 1931, in England and Wales, was the same as that of the highest group in 1911. But a statistical study of IM by social class in England and Wales has shown that class differ-ences are not only not diminishing : they are increasing. In 1911 a child in the lowest income group was three times as likely to die between the ages of six and twelve months as a child in the highest group ; in 1931 it was *five times as likely to die* as a child in the highest group. The same point can be illustrated for the period since 1931. In 1931-2 the ten English county boroughs with the highest IM had an IM 22 per cent higher than the average for the whole country ; in 1944-5 their IM was 30 per cent higher than the average. Thus although the improvement has affected all classes, it has affected least those most in need of improvement.

national IM in 1970 below 30 in favored EngTowns below 20

THE MEANING OF "STATISTICS"

This chapter, more than most, is full of numbers and per-centages. It is therefore perhaps appropriate to quote a passage from a recent publication of the British Ministry of Health :

> Statistics may be dull things and are much abused by cynics, but they have provided the starting point for many of the advances in preventive and curative medicine and they will continue to do so.

Some of the facts given earlier in this chapter illustrate this. To determine some of the main causes of rheumatic heart disease it was necessary to study sample groups of families, and to relate the incidence of the disease to

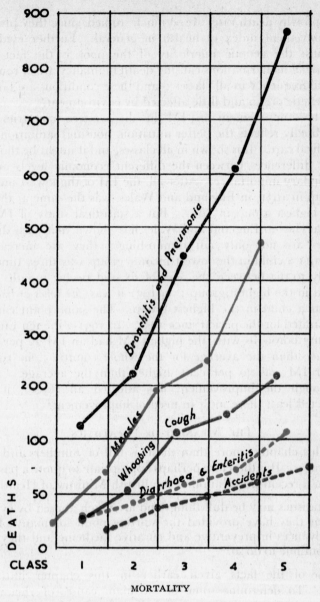

The second year : deaths in children aged 1 to 2 per 100,000 legitimate live births various factors, including economic status and over-crowding. The techniques of sampling, and of correlating one group of facts with another, come under a particular branch of mathematics, statistics, or statistical analysis. A statistician, when he uses his special methods of analysis, is taking the results of counting something—perhaps the number of persons suffering from a particular disease—and working out the significance of the results of the counting.

There is no more justification for criticising the statistician than there would be for criticising a farmer who reported that he owned 40 dairy cows, and that 30 of them (or 75 per cent) were in milk. A possible reason why many nevertheless feel a distrust of "statistics"—which generally means a distrust of general statements about large numbers of people or things—is that they are necessarily impersonal. For the statistician as such the latest group of deaths from some disease are, so to speak, just another buzz and click on the calculating machine. What is needed is to relate the results of his calculations to individual experience. It is one thing to read of the tens of millions of sufferers from chronic malaria, quite another to appreciate the suffering of these many persons, condemned throughout their lives to a debilitated existence in poverty and squalor. In discussing a community with a high infant mortality it is necessary to understand what the figures mean for the individual mothers who have to watch their babies die after a few days of vomiting and diarrhœa.

A book of this sort can do little more than report the facts of starvation or disease in general terms : the task of conveying what the facts signify, in terms of individual suffering or the relief of suffering, must be left to the journalist or the novelist writing of particular persons and incidents. The general lesson of this chapter is the immense power of modern bacteriology to prevent a great number of the worst diseases. Although there are some serious gaps, our knowledge of the causes and means of prevention of infectious disease is remarkably complete. Cholera, the dysenteries, typhoid, typhus and small-pox not only can be, but in some countries have been almost completely wiped out. Even malaria and yellow fever have been brought under control in some areas. Full application of existing knowledge could reduce tuberculosis and the main causes of death in infancy to a very small fraction of the present total. But the knowledge cannot be applied simply by the passage of laws or by government regulation. Just as food production and nutritional standards can be raised only as part of a general process of economic improvement, so the prevention of infectious disease requires vast expenditure on public health services, and education of the whole community to take advantage of them. In the long run such expenditure justifies itself not only by the increase in health and happiness, but also by the release for productive purposes of human energy which would otherwise be drained away by disease. Knowledge of these facts is especially necessary today, both to enable ordinary people to play their part in promoting their own health and that of their children, and to reinforce the demand that the greatest possible exertion should be devoted to this end.

CHAPTER 14

POPULATION

DESPITE the famine and disease which have always killed men, and which continue to kill them, human populations have enormously increased since man first appeared. And they are still increasing. Among animals in general man is relatively infertile : women bear as a rule only one child at a time, and the interval between children is seldom less than a year ; often it is much more even in the absence of deliberate contraception. Nevertheless human reproductive potential can maintain a high rate of population increase, in the absence of a corresponding mortality or of birth control. In the most favourable conditions a large human population can double itself in about 25 years. Even in times of food shortage reproduction may continue at a high rate, and so make the shortage worse, until famine occurs and numbers are reduced by starvation.

The first great increase in human numbers, as we saw in chapter 10, arose from the invention of agriculture ; before that food scarcity had severely limited human populations. In the agricultural period of the past seven thousand years food has still often been a limiting factor, but epidemic disease has also played a part in restraining population growth. Today, some populations are still increasing, while others remain roughly stationary. In the first case they may be facing famine and a greater incidence of infection, in the second, economic difficulties due to an increasing proportion of old people. In this chapter we shall consider how the various factors influencing population size actually work, and what changes are going on in the populations of various countries.

DEATH RATES

The death rate is the number of persons dying in one year, in each 1,000 of population. We find three kinds of influences affecting death rates. First, the direct causes of death may become more, or less, effective : measles, for instance, seems to have become more virulent in the past fifty years, and scarlet fever less virulent. But changes of this sort have only a minor importance. Second, death rates are influenced by changes in the resistance to the causes of death : resistance in this sense may be within the individual, as when a poor diet leads to lowered resistance, or outside—for instance sanitary measures which prevent infection. The third factor is the age-composition of a population. If a population has relatively many old people its death rate will be higher than that of a population of normal composition : some English south-coast towns, for instance, have very high death rates because many of their inhabitants have come to them on retirement at 60 or later.

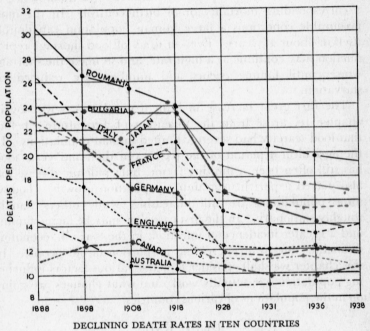

DECLINING DEATH RATES IN TEN COUNTRIES

Note that the time scale alters after 1928 in this figure

The death rates referred to above are called *crude* death rates, but when the rates of two countries are compared we use

234

standardised death rates : that is, we allow for differences in age composition. Recently the crude death rate in Sweden was 12 per thousand, while that of Australia was between 8 and 9 ; but when the rates were standardised they were found to be almost identical. So, insofar as the death rate is a measure of health, Sweden and Australia had equally good health. The reason for the lower crude rate for Australia was the presence of immigrants in the prime of life, among whom the death rate is lower than for other age groups.

In large parts of the world, but especially in the west, death rates have fallen strikingly since 1800. The most obvious cause has been improvement in the health services. Recently the rise in nutritional standards also has contributed. Other social changes have played a part : since about 1750 the availability of cheap cotton clothing, which can be washed, has made cleanliness easier and so has reduced infection. There are also political influences : wars and internal disorder tend to increase death rates, not only directly but even more by the social disruption they bring about. The political factor has probably been important in China, for instance, where the Manchu dynasty kept civil war in check from 1644 until the present century ; during this period the Chinese population increased a good deal.

One way in which mortalities can be compared is by taking the *expectation of life at birth* for different places and different times. In England and Wales in 1841 it was just over 40 years for men ; in 1891 it was 44, and in 1931 nearly 59 ; for women the figures are slightly higher. In India, between the two world wars, it was about 25. In colonial Africa it is very low, and has even fallen during this century. In these backward countries mortality is much as it was in the ancient world : the mummy cases of Roman Egypt suggest that the upper class Egyptians two thousand years ago had an expectation of life at birth of between 25 and 30 years ; there is evidence that in Rome it was only 20, but in some Roman provinces it was probably about 35. The last figure is close to some of those computed for the Middle Ages : in Breslau in 1690, for instance, it is believed to have been about 33.5.

These figures do not signify that most Indians, for example, die at about 25 : very large numbers die in the first few months of life, and most of the remainder pass the age of thirty : the expectation of life is, in fact, only an average, and can be misleading unless the death rates at different ages are kept in mind.

BIRTH RATES

The decline in death rates has been followed in some countries by a decline in birth rates. For most of the world's population, however, birth rates are near the maximum allowed by human fecundity. (Fecundity is the reproductive *capacity*, whereas fertility is the amount of reproduction actually achieved). In Japan, China, India, Java and Egypt, in Carr-Saunders' words, "marriage is early and universal, and when marriage has been consummated no steps are taken to limit the size of the family." The decline in birth rates has occurred on the whole in the countries where death rates have fallen most, and in particular where child mortality has been much reduced. Had there been no decline the populations in these countries would have increased enormously in the past century, and most parents would be faced with the upbringing of between five and twenty children. In Britain in the mid-Victorian period each couple had on an average about six children born alive. The corresponding figure by 1925-9 was 2.2.

The crude birth rate is affected by three main factors. First, as with death rates, it is influenced by the age distribution of the population : births are almost confined to women between the ages of 15 and 50, and the birth rate depends on the proportion of such women in the population. The age distribution within the child-bearing range may also have some effect, since women are most fertile in their twenties. A second factor is marriage : there will be fewer births the more women remain unmarried, or the more marriage is delayed. This has probably been important both in Europe and in the United States. In the U.S.A. the birth rate is reckoned to have fallen from 55 in 1800 to 20 in 1930 ; yet the proportion of women of child-bearing age rose during that period. Part of the explanation is an increase in the proportion of single persons, which was particularly marked in the census of 1890.

Similarly, in Britain, age at marriage has been rising since 1871. By 1911 more people were marrying at ages 25 to 29 than at 20 to 24. *now 21 for women*

But the decline of fertility in the west cannot be attributed only, or even mainly, to less marriage. The decline has been so great that the obvious explanations have seemed to be inadequate, and some fancy ones have been put forward. For example, vitamin E deficiency is known to reduce reproductive capacity in some mammals, and it has been suggested that if we ate more vitamin E we might get more babies ; but there is no evidence that we lack vitamin E : it is present in most foods. Then cleanliness has been accused of some responsibility in two ways. First, soap tends to kill human sperm and is indeed a good deal more spermicidal than some of the chemical contraceptives that have been widely used ; it has therefore been suggested that soap in the vagina may have reduced fertility. But again there is no evidence. On the other hand there is some experimental basis for the second theory. Human sperm are killed at temperatures only a little above that of the scrotum in which the testicles are suspended, and it has been shown that the application of hot water to the scrotum reduces the number of live sperm produced in subsequent ejaculations. It is therefore possible that hot baths before retiring may tend to reduce male fertility.

An entirely different suggestion attributes lowered fertility to less coitus resulting from an increase in alternative sources of enjoyment. However, it is difficult to measure the extent to which people are enjoying life, and there is no adequate evidence that enjoyment does lessen sexual activity. There is evidence, however, that the ratio of copulations to pregnancies is very high. An investigation by Pearl of 199 city-dwelling American couples under the age of 50, none using contraceptive methods, gave a ratio of 254 copulations to each pregnancy. The average number of children for each couple was 5.8—on contemporary standards quite high. These results have been much criticised and discussed, but they have not been contraverted. But there is no reason to think that the ratio has greatly changed during the time of the fall in the birth rate.

The most obvious, and probably the principal cause of the

falling birth rates is the increasing practice of contraception. Carr-Saunders has summarised the evidence. He points out that the decline of the birth rate in most countries coincided with outbursts of birth-control propaganda, and goes on :

> In almost every country the decline began in the upper economic class and spread downwards in such a fashion that there has come into being a marked negative correlation between social status and fertility.[1] This is compatible with the spread of contraception if it is supposed that the better-off people first acquired these new practices. It is in general true that fashions spread downwards ; moreover, contraceptive appliances are costly, and therefore not easily accessible to the poor.

Further evidence comes from the fertility of groups of different religious faiths. In Holland and Canada Protestant groups can be compared with Catholic, among whom birth-control (except by means of the "safe" period) is forbidden. Catholics have a much higher fertility. The relatively low fertility of the nominally Catholic populations of France and Austria is held to be due to the decline of religious belief in those countries : certainly in Austria the birth-rate in the country districts, where the church is powerful, is higher than among the more sophisticated townsfolk. Special studies support these conclusions. Carr-Saunders refers to the work of Methorst, who investigated 21,307 families in Holland.

> He discovered that, when no child had died, there was less then twelve months interval between the birth of children in only 1.4 per cent of the cases, but that when a child had died, another birth took place within twelve months in no less than 19.7 per cent. The only possible explanation is that, when a child has died, the parents seek to replace it and abandon . . . birth-control for a time. Again, . . . Stevenson showed that, whereas in general the fertility of young wives sank from the age of twenty onwards, the fertility of young wives of the professional class rose until they were over 25. Owing to the late age at which professional men begin to earn a living, there are strong motives for using birth-control among very young professional couples

[1] But see p. 249.

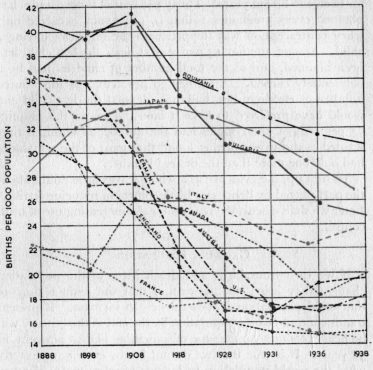

DECLINING BIRTH RATES IN TEN COUNTRIES

Note that the time scale alters after 1928 in this figure

when first married ; that they do so is the only possible
explanation of this curious anomaly.

Actually, there is an alternative explanation for Methorst's
results. The chances of conception are, for physiological
reasons, reduced while a mother is suckling a child, and so the
early loss of an infant increases the likelihood of a fresh conception. In some primitive societies it is usual for a child to be
fed at the breast until three or more years old, and this practice
seems to have a use in preventing an excessive birth-rate.

An American investigation gives direct evidence on family
planning in one group. White protestant couples of good
education were studied in Indianopolis ; all had been married

for twelve to fifteen years.   Thirty per cent of these couples had planned every pregnancy : that is, pregnancy occurred only when contraception was stopped with the object of having a child.   Among another 14 per cent at least the last child had been planned, and so the total number of children had been deliberately chosen.   A further 30 per cent had the wanted number of children, but had not planned the last child and would have preferred to have it later.   Thus in this enquiry 74 per cent of the couples had the number of children they wanted ; and it was further found that most of the remainder had only one more than the desired number.

To sum up, the evidence as a whole leaves little doubt about the part played by deliberate birth control in reducing fertility. Later we shall discuss the reasons for the increasing use of birth control.

GROWING POPULATIONS

If we turn from birth and death rates to the population changes they bring about, we find that the main feature of the world population is its tendency to increase.   If present trends continue world population by the end of the century will be near 3,000m. an increase of something like 50 per cent in 50 years.   It is true that we do not know, even now, exactly what the world population is, but we have estimates of tolerable accuracy covering the last three centuries.   In this period there has been what Carr-Saunders has called "an unparalleled outburst of population".   The total number of human beings has increased nearly four times.   The increase has taken place in all continents, though it has been greatest among Europeans who have increased seven times ; only they have overflowed in large numbers, especially to North America, and there are now 200m. outside Europe.

The 2,200m. human beings are very unevenly distributed throughout the world.   Europe, with 520m., is densely populated, and parts of Asia, with its total of more than half that of the world, also have dense populations.   The Americas are more thinly occupied : North America has 155m. and Central and South America about 20 and 85m. respectively.   The population of Africa is estimated to be 145m., a relatively

Table 3

ESTIMATED WORLD POPULATION AND DISTRIBUTION BY CONTINENTS: 1800-1939

	1800	1850	1900	1913	1939
	Population in millions				
WORLD ..	919	1,091	1,527	1,723	2,080
Asia	600	664	839	923	1,097
Europe	188	266	390	468	542
Africa	100	100	141	135	157
N. and Central America ..	15	39	110	134	184
South America	14	20	41	56	89
Oceania	2	2	6	8	11
	Percentage distribution				
WORLD	100.0	100.0	100.0	100.0	100.0
Asia	65.3	60.9	54.9	53.6	52.7
Europe	20.5	24.4	25.5	27.2	26.1
Africa	10.9	9.2	9.2	7.8	7.5
N. and Central America ..	1.6	3.6	7.2	7.8	8.8
South America	1.5	1.8	2.7	3.2	4.3
Oceania	0.2	0.2	0.4	0.5	0.5

Many of the figures in this table are necessarily only approximations, especially the earlier ones. China in particular, which now probably accounts for one-fourth to one-fifth of the world's population, has not yet had any adequate census : even today estimates of the Chinese population are based on nothing better than sample censuses of relatively small areas.

Although the total increase in the population of Asia in the past 150 years has been about 500m. its relative increase has been less than that of any other continent except Africa. Potential increase in both these continents has been checked by famine and pestilence. The enormous relative expansion in North and Central America, and to a less extent in South America, has been due to the emigration of Europeans who have subsequently rapidly increased in numbers. Correspondingly, the percentage of Asiatics and Africans in the world total has diminished, but there is no reason to think that this trend will continue small figure for a large continent. (These figures are slightly more up-to-date than those of table 2). The densely settled areas are southern China, India, Europe and eastern North America. These areas all have fertile soil, adequate rainfall, navigable rivers, and coal and iron, and are well placed for trade.

The current increase in world population is not due to a uniform increase going on in all countries. It is due largely to the growth of the populations of India and Indonesia. Some smaller nations, such as Egypt and Ceylon, are also growing rapidly, and even Europe had 21m. more people in 1947 than in 1939 ; this was due mainly to increases in S.E. Europe. Of all these India has the largest population, and has been most studied. Since the first world war India has shown a steady reduction in mortality, and this will become more marked if the health services proposed since the second world war are made to work. During the 20 years from 1921 the population of India increased by 83m., and this rate of increase could, according to an official report published in 1946, easily be doubled if the health services were improved without a corresponding reduction in fertility. And there is no present indication of a decline in fertility : it is true that as early as 1924 the birth-rate among the Brahmins living in Madras was no higher than that of the Europeans, but Brahmins belong to a very small, privileged section of the community, and drastic social changes would be required in India before their example could be followed by a majority of the population. The following estimated birth and death-rates for India illustrate the position.

	birth-rate	death-rate
1881–91	49	41
1891–1901	46	44
1901–11	49	43
1911–21	48	47
1921–31	46	36
1931–41	45	31

If these trends continue we may expect the present Indian population of about 400m. to become 730m. in 30 years, that is, by about 1980. For the whole of this number to be adequately fed, food production in India will have to be nearly three times as great as it is now.

There is a similar situation in Indonesia. In Java, for instance, the population was about 4.5m. in 1815, 28.4m. in 1928, and about 50m. in 1945.

These are countries in which neither birth nor death rates have come under secure control. The same applies to China, and to many of the South American countries. But in these, as far as we know, death rates are not falling as in India and Indonesia : they remain high, and in step with the high birth rates. Consequently the tendency to increase in numbers remains only latent. China, which is believed to have a population of the order of 400m., may show a very rapid population growth when health services, such as were introduced into Western Europe in the nineteenth century, become widespread. Up to now the Chinese population has shown violent fluctuations due to famines and epidemics, without any steady trend up or down.

There is one further large population which is still increasing rapidly, that of the U.S.S.R. It differs from those so far mentioned in having both death and birth rates declining. It has been estimated that the birth rate in 1927 was 45.0, whereas by 1938 it had fallen to 38.3. The death rate had however shown a greater fall, from 26.0 to 17.8.

DECLINING POPULATIONS?

Although their death rates are low, western Europe, North America and the British Dominions have nearly stationary populations. In these countries birth rates have fallen enough at least to balance the much lowered death rates ; if this were not the case the peoples of these countries would have a standard of living more like that of the backward peoples. The decline of fertility in the West, and among European populations generally, has led to a good deal of discussion of what has been called "race suicide", the "invention of sterility" and so on. Since about 1930 the main population problem has been represented as the "twilight of parenthood" or the "parents' revolt". It might be thought that the attainment of a stationary population when the death rate had been so much reduced

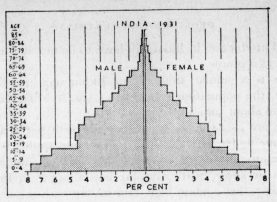

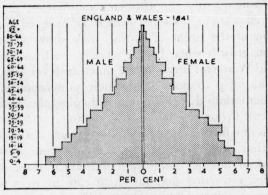

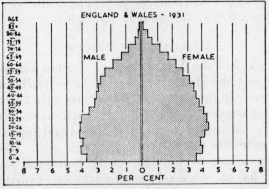

AGE AND POPULATION

Age pyramids for India (1931) and England & Wales (1841 and 1931). In 1841 England and Wales had a population with an age distribution rather like that of India today, with a high proportion of very young people ; the diagram for England and Wales in 1931 shows the effect of the heavy decline in birth-rate : there are still plenty of people in middle life, but they are producing far fewer children would be a source of satisfaction. That it has been instead a source of alarm is due to the fear that the populations of the countries listed in table 4 (page 246) would fall rapidly : the apparent stability was thought to be illusory.

The prediction that European populations must decline depends on the study of the *net reproduction rates* of these populations. The net reproduction rate measures the extent to which a population is replacing itself. The need for a special means of measuring replacement can be illustrated by an example. Suppose an area, say an island, were newly settled entirely by men and women of between 20 and 45. The number of births per 100 persons in such a population would be exceptionally high, since every individual would be in the reproductive phase. There would also be a very low death rate, and so the population would increase rapidly. The rate of increase would, however, fall off as some of the original population grew old, and as the proportion of children increased. It might indeed turn out that, despite the initially high increase, the birth rate had not been high enough to maintain the population indefinitely at a steady level. For stability each mother must be replaced by another mother. This does not signify that each family should, on the average, consist of one daughter and one son : there is mortality to be allowed for, and the fact that some women never have any children. It is calculated that, in western Europe, for replacement to be assured, each couple who produce children should have, on the average, nearly four. Given this, the net reproduction rate would be approximately 1.0—the figure that represents a fertility rate just high enough to keep the population constant.

Table 4 shows that a number of countries have or had net reproduction rates of less than one. France, indeed, where the net reproduction has been below unity since the beginning of the century, has already begun its population decline (if we ignore the effects of immigration). An important question is whether there will be a decline elsewhere. Certainly, if the trends of the 1930's had continued for long the decline in some countries would be startling. The population of the United Kingdom today is about 45m. Ignoring the effects of emigration and immigration, and assuming the maintenance of pre-

Table 4

COUNTRIES WITH NET REPRODUCTION RATES NEAR UNITY

COUNTRY	YEAR	N.R.R.
U.S.A.	1937	0.965
	1942	1.189
United Kingdom	1937	0.785
	1944	0.990
France	1939	0.9
Belgium	1939	0.859
	1941	0.672
Denmark	1937	0.947
	1943	1.140
Germany	1940	0.976
Austria	1939	1.00
Hungary	1938	1.00
Czechoslovakia	1929-32	0.94
Norway	1939	0.856
Sweden	1941	0.843
Switzerland	1938	0.779
	1943	1.054
Australia	1937	0.981
	1943	1.163
New Zealand	1937	0.999
	1942	1.208
Estonia	1938	0.79
Finland	1938	0.96
Latvia	1939	0.99

war trends, it would be about 31m. in 1975 and 4.5m. in 2035.

Figures such as these must not be regarded as prophecies : they show only what would happen if the rates of a particular period continued unchanged. The likelihood of the maintenance of particular trends cannot be accurately assessed, because of the many influences which affect the birth-rate. The way in which net reproduction rates may mislead can be illustrated by a calculation made in 1935, that the population of England and Wales would be 40.14m. in 1947 if the prevailing trends continued. The actual population in 1947 was 43.02m. Moreover, the calculations made in 1935 suggested that by 1945 the population would be decreasing at the rate of 125,000 a year ; but in fact, the excess of births over deaths in the first half of 1947 alone was 176,000. A recent prediction, made in the report of the Royal Commission on Population, is that a further slow increase in the population of England and Wales must be expected, and that this may continue for a generation.

The rise in fertility during the 1940's has been common to a number of very diverse European countries, including Eire, Czechoslovakia, France and the Scandinavian nations. Various explanations have been suggested, including full employment, and better health among the young men and women who became mature during this period. There is little direct evidence on what factors have actually been most important.

Although we cannot predict future populations with any precision, we can get some idea of the motives which have led people to limit their families. Above we saw that birth-control, rather than any increase in sterility, has been the probable means of family limitation, and it might be thought that the decline in fertility has been simply due to the spread of knowledge of contraceptive methods. But many enquiries have shown that the most used method even today is *coitus interruptus,* in which the semen is not discharged until the penis is withdrawn ; and this method (frowned on by psychologists) must have been known for as long as the connexion between coitus and conception has been understood. The spread of knowledge of contraceptive methods has probably contributed, as we saw earlier, but it seems unlikely that it was the primary cause.

The most obvious motive for family limitation is the burden imposed on women by a large family. J. S. Mill wrote :

> The family is rarely a large one by the woman's desire, because upon her weighs, besides all the physical suffering and a full share in all privations, the unbearable domestic toil which grows from a large number of children.

But this was written at a time when, nevertheless, families remained large. Children were, until very recently, an economic asset to their parents. Apart from their ability to work when still very young they would probably be their parents' only support in old age. This seems to have been the origin of the practice, still kept up in some parts even of England, of a young couple awaiting the pregnancy of the woman before marrying. Today the economic motive for having a large family is much reduced : the lowered death rate makes it unnecessary to ensure the survival of one or two by having a large number ; and old-age pensions and other social services reduce the likelihood of complete destitution even for the childless. Most parents reduce the size of their families but do not voluntarily remain completely childless : the aim seems to be to have perhaps two or three children, but not more. (This disposes of such explanations as "fear of war" for family limitation.) Alvar Myrdal, in her analysis of the family in Sweden, emphasises the probable importance of the higher standards of child care now expected, and of the heavy financial cost of maintaining these standards. In a recent survey in Britain the average age of mothers at the birth of a first child was found to be 26 in the most fertile income group, and even higher in other groups. The delay is evidently due to waiting until a certain income level or degree of security has been achieved.

From this point of view it may seem an anomaly that the decline of the birth rate begins among those with higher incomes, that is, among those who could presumably best afford a large family. A possible explanation is that, since family limitation was contrary to established convention, it was, in Alvar Myrdal's words,

> only to be expected that those social groups that were most mobile and already most emancipated from the static scales

of values should first start consciously to consider their childbearing. Thus family limitation is not a function of families being richer. All the instances generally quoted of "the richer the family, the fewer the children" relate only to a transition period, when the upper classes have temporary precedence in utilizing methods of family limitation.

This explanation, though mainly speculative, is supported by the fact that the reproductive decline has, by the middle of the century, spread to all economic classes. In fact, in Sweden, the tendency is now said to be for the richer families to have the larger numbers of children.

It seems likely, therefore, that in the countries with net reproduction rates of approximately unity family size is becoming stabilised in all classes at a low level. Various attempts have been made to prevent or to arrest this decline in fertility. In France, the country with the lowest net reproduction rate, a much-discussed system of family allowances was introduced during the first world war and made the subject of a law in 1932. The allowances have been estimated to cover about a half of the cost of each child. They did not prevent the continued decline in fertility, though they may have reduced it. Much the same applies to Italy, where there were a bachelor tax, and a higher income tax rate on bachelors and the childless, as well as family allowances. In Germany under the Nazis a number of minor measures were introduced, including marriage loans : there was a temporary increase in births, but no evidence of any long-term effect. In the United Kingdom small allowances for second and subsequent children were introduced in 1945. Two years later a report on childbearing in Britain, based on a nationwide enquiry, commented as follows :

The costs of childbearing are so high that they are likely to deter many mothers, of all classes, from having children. It is not unlikely that, in many working-class families, this expenditure has to be met by borrowing or drawing upon savings. A substantial reduction in the costs of having a child is only likely to be achieved by lowering the price of baby clothes and equipment.

We may ask whether it will not be necessary also to reduce

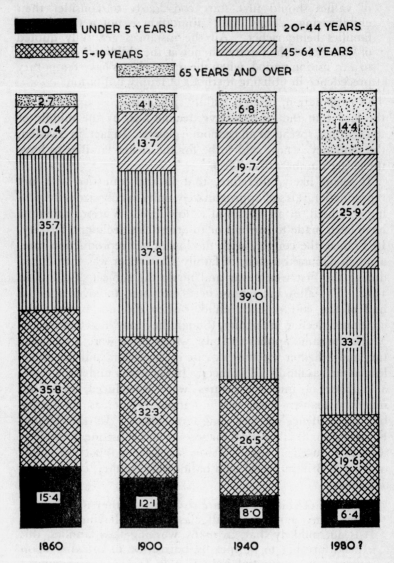

UNDER 5 YEARS 20-44 YEARS
5-19 YEARS 45-64 YEARS
65 YEARS AND OVER

AGEING POPULATION

The effect of the decline in birth and death rates on the proportion
of people in different age groups in the U.S.A. The figures for 1980
are estimates based on trends in the 1940's. There is an increase in
the proportion of old people

the rents of larger houses and to increase their number, and to make the bringing up of children more tolerable by increasing services such as home helps and nursery schools. Security of employment may also turn out to be important. In 1949 the Report of the Royal Commission on Population commented on the "economic and other handicaps of parenthood" of the period from 1910 onwards :

It remained true throughout the period that for most families the addition of children involved a substantial reduction of the family's standard of living, that the greater the number of children the smaller the chances of each child (and of the parents) of advancing in the competitive struggle and the greater the chances of falling back, and that some of the non-monetary costs of parenthood—the discomforts and risks of pregnancy and childbirth, additions to domestic work, restrictions on freedom, demands on nervous energy—increased more than proportionately with the size of the family. This is true despite the solid gains in human welfare that were achieved since the middle of the 19th century. Indeed, in the process of social advance, the position of parents and of members of larger families relative to others grew worse. The standard of living of the mass of the people rose, leisure increased . . . but the gap between parents and non-parents widened.

It is remarkable that the government which has adopted the most drastic population policy is that of the U.S.S.R., a country with a net reproduction rate still far above unity. In 1926 the rate was 1.72, and it has evidently not fallen greatly since then. Today the population of the U.S.S.R. is less than 200m., but at its present rate of increase it will reach about 300m. by the end of the century. The proportion of young people will be far higher, and of old people far lower, than in the countries of western Europe. Nevertheless, in 1944 a law was passed "On increasing state aid to expectant mothers, mothers of large families, and unmarried mothers, protection of motherhood and childhood . . .". The new measures included various grants and allowances for children, the expansion of privileges for expectant and nursing mothers, and taxes on single men and women and persons with small families. Various orders and awards were also instituted for mothers with large numbers of children, such as are given in most countries for rather different forms of public service.

FUTURE POPULATIONS

If the Soviet government is successful in maintaining a satisfactory reproduction rate, its population policy will have important implications for other countries. (It has already been strongly urged that its example should be followed in Australia, to prevent an expected decline in the Australian population.) Every population may be regarded as having a place in a cycle of changes in which the ratio of births to deaths alters in an orderly manner. The population policy of a country must depend on its position in the cycle.

The *demographic cycle,* as it is called, has five phases. The *first phase* is one in which both birth and death rates are very high : in times of peace and abundance the population rises ; famine, pestilence and war at other times cause decreases. There is no steady trend up or down. China is the only large country which has up to now remained in this phase. In the *second phase* better social organisation leads to a fall in the death rate, while the birth rate remains high ; the population increases, though not rapidly. India, Indonesia, most of South and Central America, and the whole of Africa except Abyssinia and South Africa, are in this phase. In the *third phase* the death rate declines still further, and although the birth rate also tends to fall the rate of population increase is high. The U.S.S.R., Japan and the countries of southern and eastern Europe are in this phase. With the *fourth phase* approximate stability is reached with both birth and death rates low. The net reproduction rate is about unity ; not only does the population show no marked trend up or down, but, unlike a population in the first phase, it also escapes violent fluctuation. Countries in this phase are shown in table 4. Finally we come to the *fifth phase* : this is largely hypothetical, since only one country, France, has ever reached it, and today the French population appears to be returning to the fourth phase. In the fifth phase the fall in the birth rate is so great that the population, despite a low death rate, declines steadily.

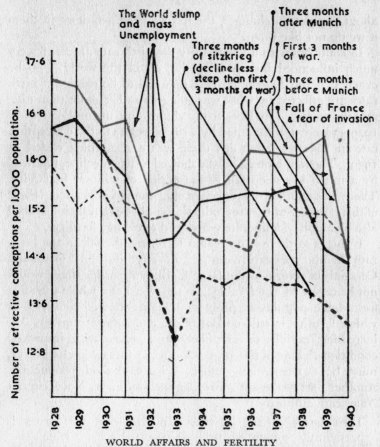

WORLD AFFAIRS AND FERTILITY

Influence of world events on effective conception rate in England and Wales. The diagram is based on the number of live births. Broken blue line represents January-March in each year; broken red, April-June; continuous red, July-September; continuous blue, October-December

It will be noticed that the U.S.S.R. is only in the third phase, but that the attempt is already being made there to avoid the fifth, and to ensure for some time a steady population increase despite greater industrialism and a rising standard of life. This policy is based on the view that scientific and technical advances in food production can more than balance the needs of the growing population. A further implication is that there is nothing inevitable in the population cycle : the more we know

253

about population changes, the less we need acquiesce in them if we do not like them.

In countries with a low fertility the birth rate at least is very much influenced by what is going on in the world. To be exact, it is the conception rate that has to be studied : birth rates are affected by what was going on rather more than nine months earlier. In Britain the slump and unemployment of 1929-33 were accompanied by a steep decline in the conception rate in 1931-3 ; after this there was a rise which ended in 1939. The first months of war showed a steep decline, followed by a much less steep fall in the period of military inactivity. There was another steep decline after the fall of France. Facts of this sort suggest that reproduction could be rapidly influenced also by a policy deliberately designed to change fertility.

If this is so there is no reason to regard the fall in the birth rate in the western countries as anything but fortunate. Certainly a return to the large families of earlier times would not be regarded as tolerable. In the world as a whole the most formidable population problem remains that of countries in which fertility is still uncontrolled, and where numbers are increasing rapidly or are likely to increase with improved conditions. Part of the answer to this, as we saw in chapter 11, must be a tremendous effort to increase food production. Another part of the answer is suggested by F. W. Notestein, an American authority :

> The matter cannot be rigidly proved, but the writer is profoundly convinced that only a society in which the individual (child or adult) has a reasonable chance for survival in healthy life will develop that interest in the dignity and material well-being of the individual essential to the reduction of fertility. He therefore firmly believes in directly fostering public health *as part of the program required to reduce growth potential.*

To sum up, in the past famine and epidemic disease have limited populations, and in times of plenty man was at the mercy of his own fecundity. Today we know how to produce much more food and to prevent much disease ; we are also beginning to learn how to control reproduction. For most of the world the question is, when will the knowledge be put to use ?

CHAPTER 15

SUMMING UP

> The philosophers have only *interpreted* the
> world in various ways ; the point however
> is to *change* it.
>
> KARL MARX

IN the first chapter biology was described as knowledge
that has come largely from man's efforts to produce food and to
prevent disease. This view of science, as a product of society
as a whole, is in contradiction to the one which represents
science as the product of a few inspired minds, functioning in
isolation and studying "nature" or "truth" for its own sake.
It is true that scientific advance depends to an important
extent on the work of a few people with a special talent for
discovery and interpretation. But the work of such people is
often very closely and obviously related to the human needs of
their own time and country. Pasteur, for example, was one of
the greatest of experimental biologists, and all his major
contributions to knowledge had an immediate application,
though at the same time he and his colleagues made an advance
in theoretical biology that was of the first importance. Pasteur
is most famous for helping to found the science of bacteriology,
and for showing the way to prevent a good deal of human
disease ; but a great part of his work was inspired, directly
or indirectly, by the needs of French agriculture and the wine
industry, and he gave them valuable help.

Not all scientific work is related so closely and obviously
to immediate needs. The other leading figure of nineteenth
century biology was Charles Darwin, and it might seem that
his theory of evolution had nothing to do with his social
background. But close examination of his work, and the times
he lived in, make it clear that he was not functioning in an
intellectual vacuum. The theory of the origin of species by
natural selection was arrived at, not only by Darwin, but also
simultaneously by Alfred Russell Wallace working independently. Simultaneous discovery by independent workers is a

common feature of the development of science, and it is almost invariably true that whenever a major advance is made it is the product of the work of a number of scientists, working more or less independently on similar lines. This at once suggests that scientific advance is part of a general historical process, and is not due to the fortuitous appearance of isolated geniuses. In the case of Darwin and the theory of evolution it is a striking fact that the idea of organic evolution—which had been put forward by various biologists for a century before Darwin— came to be accepted at a time of especially rapid social change.

Both Darwin and Wallace were led to think of natural selection as the main cause of evolution by reading the work of Malthus (referred to in chapter 11) on human populations. One of the implications of Malthus' theories was that it was useless to try to raise the living standards of the poor, since they would then only breed more rapidly and so exhaust the food supply. This outlook fitted well with the attitude of the rising capitalists of the nineteenth century : their attitude was, every man for himself and the most enterprising will come to the top and rightly earn the greatest power and wealth. There is a close analogy between this theory of how human society should work and the theory of natural selection, or "survival of the fittest", which Darwin and Wallace applied to organisms in general. Natural selection has indeed been invoked as a support for the policy of "devil take the hindmost" among human beings, although the fallacy in the argument is obvious enough : it is that even if natural selection operates throughout the organic world it does not at all follow that it operates in human society ; and even if it did, we need not acquiesce in its doing so. Most people will agree that a cut-throat struggle between individuals is unlikely to be anything but destructive of organised society.

One further fact (out of many) may serve to bring home the way in which Darwinism reflected the ideas of the times : some years before Darwin's major work, *The Origin of Species*, was published, Herbert Spencer put forward a theory of the survival of the fittest, as he called it, to support the prevailing views on human social relations. Thus a theory similar to Darwin's had already been advanced in the field of sociology.

To say that Darwin's work reflected the contemporary state

of society, or was influenced by it, is not to detract from Darwin's achievement. His work was enormous in quantity and brilliant in content. Scientists are not remote and isolated individuals : they grow up in a particular environment like anybody else, they have parents who usually hold views which belong to their own times, and teachers who give conventional instruction. They are part of the society in which they live. Darwin and Pasteur exemplify a general rule in the relations of science to society.

Progress in the application of technical knowledge depends on the use made of the abilities of especially gifted persons, such as Pasteur and Darwin, together with those of many less able men and women. These abilities include the passion for enquiry which is sometimes represented as the main driving force of scientific advance. It is one force, but its scope is limited by the extent to which those who possess it are allowed to give vent to it. Today this depends on two things. First, a child with potential scientific ability can use it only if parents or government pay for a lengthy education. Second, if his particular gifts are directed towards one line of enquiry, say, the study of moulds, he will still be unable to apply them fully unless it is thought by the government (or by some other body with funds) that the study of moulds deserves support. This particular example is taken because penicillin, one of the most valuable of chemical agents for preventing or curing infections, is produced by a mould ; and it happens that in Britain the study of moulds and other fungi has been, and is, seriously neglected. If this were not the case use might have been made of penicillin soon after it was originally discovered in London in 1929, instead of more than a decade later. This would have involved the employment of a number of botanists, chemists and medical scientists whose talents during that period may in fact have been not so profitably used.

Biological science today, in fact, is still, as it was in earlier times, largely a product of the efforts of men to get what they want. This is true even though there are a few men and women who are able to study it without any practical end in view, and not consciously influenced by the society in which they live.

Whatever the motives or motivation of scientists, most people will wish to know what direct use their work is for everyday purposes. The most fundamental contribution of biology to the study of man is a general law which has been exemplified in almost every chapter. Every individual is the product of a complex development, in which the effects of the genes and of outside influences are continually interacting : neither heredity nor environment can be said to be the more important, though one may have more influence than the other in causing variation in particular characters. If we are considering differences—physical or mental—between races, classes or the sexes, this interaction has to be allowed for. When it is allowed for we find that "human nature" is much more varied and changeable than has commonly been supposed. "Races" are found to be both exceedingly heterogeneous genetically, and capable of very rapid changes from generation to generation : that is, they include people with all sorts of potentialities, and the expression of these potentialities varies with social organisation. In palæolithic society there was little opportunity for the expression of many of the qualities we most admire today, except some manual dexterity and, in certain periods, skill in the visual arts ; the appropriate genes must have been available, but an environment in which they could have full effect had not been evolved. All we know at present suggests that any human group, in an appropriate environment, is capable of producing individuals with a high level of technical skill, artistic ability and social sense.

Just as there is no monopoly of virtue among races, so economic or social classes are found to be of very mixed heredity ; they are indeed even less permanent and less sharply marked off from each other than the racial groups, and ability is lost if the children of any group are forbidden access to education, or to particular trades or professions, on account of the poverty or social status of their parents. In most societies, moreover, the female sex as a whole occupies, quite unjustly, an inferior social position.

Although heredity and environment are of equivalent importance in determining the course of individual development, they are not of equal importance when we come to action.

258

There is little to be done to alter human genetic constitutions (though it is a different matter with domestic animals) : if we find a group of persons of poor physique, low mental ability or criminal tendencies we must seek to alter the environment in which the group has developed. The outstanding contributions of biology to the improvement of environment have been the increase of food supplies, the knowledge of nutrition and the demonstration of the origin and method of prevention of many diseases.

The emphasis on environment as alterable, while heredity is regarded as practically fixed, may seem to conflict with the second great biological principle which we have applied to man. Just as each individual is a product of heredity and environment, so mankind as a whole is a product of evolution. And evolution depends on the survival of some genetic constitutions and the disappearance of others. But the genetic changes in populations occur on a quite different time scale from that of the changes in human society, if we except those in domestic animals under controlled breeding. *Homo sapiens* has barely had time to show even slight evolutionary change in the biological sense in the whole of the 70,000 years during which he is known to have existed ; yet in less than ten thousand years he has evolved socially from savagery to civilisation, and civilisation itself has taken on a series of progressively more complex forms. Today social change has become even more rapid and more drastic, as a result of the application of scientific knowledge and methods to the solution of a limited range of problems. Apart from food and sanitation these problems have been mostly those of power, transport and communications, and of the mass production of goods, such as clothes, which had formerly been made individually by craftsmen or in the home.

But now it is realised that scientific methods can be applied to a much wider range of problems. For instance, we no longer have to take for granted traditional building methods : in the words of one report, "At present, . . . we drag more than 100 tons of material to the site of every house, when less than 5 tons would produce a house that would be much warmer and take less coal to heat it." Inside the house the kitchen can be designed so that it fully meets the convenience of those who work in it, cooking can be done with little or no destruction of food content, and food can be kept without suffering decay or infection with disease germs. Similarly, in the factory, the methods of operational research can be applied to minimise fatigue, danger of injury and loss of time ; and this is not only a matter of such obvious things as ventilation and lighting, but may extend to the colour of the paint and whether workers should listen to music while they work.

Advances of this sort often depend on research requiring the help of laymen in large numbers. And once the research has been done the intelligent collaboration of the public is even more necessary. Diphtheria immunisation is a notable example of what has already been achieved. Science is still often regarded as something remote—the property of a select few whose knowledge the majority of people cannot hope to share and whose outlook ordinary men would not think of adopting. The barriers are today being broken down as the role and scope of scientific knowledge become more obvious to non-scientists, and as the scientists themselves become increasingly involved in the social and political turmoil.

The business of making the whole of society scientific has begun in a few countries with the acquisition of a general understanding of the nature of infectious disease ; and, in the physical sciences, with the development of popular knowledge of, for instance, electricity. But there is still nowhere a widespread understanding of scientific method, even among those with a superior education, and there will probably be none until children have the opportunity to practise it in school. At present education remains in the pre-scientific phase : we are told what we ought to think, instead of having to discover things for ourselves and exercise our powers of criticism. It is likely that parents who have recently co-operated in the mass testing of vaccines have learnt more of scientific method in doing so than they did throughout their schooling. In one group of tests, in which the parents of seven English boroughs co-operated, new whooping-cough vaccines were on trial : some thousands of infants were injected, one half with a vaccine and the remainder, the "control" group, with a mixture outwardly similar but not containing the material under test. Neither the parents nor the doctors who administered the vaccines knew which was which : all injections were numbered, and the key was kept by the Medical Research Council. Two years after injection each child was observed again, and a comparison made of the incidence of whooping-cough in the various groups : if an experimental group shows a much lower incidence than the control, that is evidence for the effectiveness of the vaccine given. It is now reported that one vaccine in particular shows great promise. The investigation illustrates the need for working with large numbers, and the need for controls and for other rigorous precautions. When this sort of thing is generally understood it will no longer be possible for a responsible adult to take a patent medicine for some complaint, and to attribute his eventual recovery to the medicine without any other evidence of its efficacy.

Just as scientific advance leads to questioning of conventions about, say, housing and food, so it may also prevent us from taking moral ideas for granted. Waddington has said :

> The contribution which science has to make to ethics, . . . merely by revealing facts which were previously unknown or commonly overlooked, is very much greater than is usually admitted. The adoption of methods of thought which are commonplaces in science would bring before the bar of ethical judgment whole groups of phenomena which do not appear there now. For instance, our ethical notions are fundamentally based on a system of individual responsibility for individual acts. The principle of statistical correlation between two sets of events, although accepted in scientific practice, is not usually felt to be ethically completely valid. If a man hits a baby on the head with a hammer, we prosecute him for cruelty or murder ; but if he sells dirty milk and the infant sickness or death rate goes up, we merely fine him for contravening the health laws. And the ethical point is taken even less seriously when the responsibility, as well as the results of the crime, falls on a statistical assemblage. The whole community of England and Wales kills 8,000 babies a year by failing to bring its infant mortality rate down to the level reached by Oslo as early as 1931, which would be perfectly feasible ; but few people seem to think this a crime.

While for many such ideas are quite new, for some they may already seem nothing but common sense. Science itself has indeed been defined as organised common sense. But getting general agreement on new attitudes is not simply a matter of the steady spread of knowledge, as education becomes more widespread and more fitted to contemporary needs. There is no walk-over for common sense. It is not only ignorance nor even conservatism that has to be overcome : there is also active opposition.

There are plenty of examples from the subject matter of this book. Lies about race differences are promulgated by those who wish to use subject groups as a source of cheap labour, or for a background for wars of conquest. Class differences are said to be inherited and fixed, by those who profit from the existence of a privileged class with economic and political power over the rest. Food and patent medicine manufacturers advertise their products with misleading statements about their chemical composition and lies about the working of the body and the causes of disease. This propaganda has full scope in at least the advertisement columns of the daily newspapers ; moreover the newspaper proprietors often depend financially on the advertisers and cannot as a rule afford to expose them even if they wish to do so. Education rarely provides an antidote : teachers are as much victims of the prevailing propaganda as parents and pupils, and usually do little more than reflect the ideas of the community to which they belong.

The full application of the modern knowledge of human biology, as of science in general, is impossible while there remain powerful groups with vested interests in ignorance and unscientific ideas. Throughout human history there are instances of drastic changes in social organisation accompanying technical advances. The transition from primitive communism to government by priest-kings over populations of slaves and peasants followed the development of agriculture. In the west states based on slavery collapsed and gave place to serfdom in a feudal society at the same time as new techniques in agriculture and other production came to be used. Feudalism in turn was replaced by capitalism when the physical sciences were applied to industrial production. In the same way, today, the application of science for human good demands further social change.

The application of biology calls for changes in at least two ways. In the first place food production by modern methods depends on very large scale planning and organisation: it cannot be done by peasants working small plots independently, and in a chronic state of indebtedness to money-lenders or banks. Even in the United States, where farms are large, the problems of soil erosion have obliged the farmers and other producers in some large areas to accept communal enterprise. The problem of food production today is, in fact, a problem for society as a whole, and not for the family or village or the individual landowner. This is an example of the economic implications of applied biology. There are many others. In the second place, the application of scientific knowledge to food production and disease prevention requires an educated people in which all adults are capable of taking an active part in these social enterprises. We could not hope for such a population anywhere if in each country there were large groups of people genetically so inferior that they could not profit from a modern education. We have seen that there is no evidence for the existence of such inferior groups ; yet even now, in the world as a whole, only a very small minority have access to learning. (All the readers of this book belong to this minority.) These facts lead to the second major social implication of the application of biology, or indeed of science in general : we cannot make use of science properly while small privileged minorities have a monopoly of knowledge. To get the full benefit of existing knowledge we must be rid of the social or economic divisions into classes as they exist in most countries today. We shall then destroy at the same time the smaller groups, mentioned above, whose positive interest it is to promote ignorance.

We may take an example of the effects of such a change from the most obvious place in which to look for instances of conflict between classes, big industry. Large employers of labour often have experts to advise them on methods of reducing the human work involved in production, and they employ such methods as "time and motion study" which have, or can have, a sound scientific basis. These methods are often in Britain and the United States strongly opposed by the trade unions, on grounds such as the excessive speed-up which they impose on the workers. Yet it is clear that scientific method could be used to make it easier and pleasanter for workers to perform their tasks, provided it were applied with regard to their interests.

We are far from applying science fully to humanitarian ends today. Lord Boyd Orr, on the eve of his retirement from the position of Director-General of the Food and Agriculture Organisation, said :

> If the food problem is not solved there will be chaos in the world in the next fifty years. The nations of the world are insane, they are spending one-third of their national incomes preparing for the next war. They are applying their energies to building up a war machine instead of applying the world's steel and industrial production to conserving the resources of the land. That is the only basis of civilisation.

Two years after the end of the second world war, of £110m. spent by Britain in a year on scientific research and development, £67m. was devoted to war science; and the proportion in the United States was almost exactly the same. Since then in both countries the proportion has risen. Until scientific work is planned for peace, and not war, we can hardly hope to make much progress towards a prosperous, egalitarian world society.

It must not be thought that the society to which we look forward is a vision of a scientific utopia peopled by robots. It is the tedious, automatic tasks that can most easily be done by the machines, and the more this happens the greater will be the demand for individual enterprise and ability.

A part of mankind has already been liberated from the toil from sunrise to sunset which has been the lot of most men and women since agriculture began ; but many of those so freed have been forced to work as long hours in worse conditions in industry, and to live in conditions of unprecedented squalor in industrial towns. Today, however, we have the technical knowledge needed to free men from slavery to production.

To make the fullest use of the liberty so acquired men and women must first have the basic essentials of food, good health and shelter. But they must also have access to the refinements of civilised life, and here too scientific knowledge has a fundamental contribution to make.

Apart from the fact that science is itself an integral part of the culture of today, it makes possible the diffusion of knowledge of all kinds. The printing press made possible the spread of literacy (still very far from complete throughout the world), and the production of written works for popular use. The development of various forms of democracy also depended on it. Today radio and the cinema are taking us, or are at least capable of taking us, several steps further.

Applied science, in fact, can, not only increase our material wealth, but also give us greater access to learning and the arts. Human biology can further this process by giving information both on human *abilities* and human *needs*. Chapters 7 to 9 have given some idea of what we already know of the diversity of human abilities. As for needs, chapters 11 to 13 have shown not only how knowledge of nutrition and health protection has accumulated, but also how appropriate action has been taken in some countries.

It is indeed only in action that the full implications of human biology can be learnt. Many will grasp the fallacies of race theory more easily by working with men and women of different colour, than by reading books about it. Members of a privileged class will appreciate the abilities to be found among the unprivileged majority by working with them on some joint enterprise. The facts of nutrition or infectious disease are brought home to many for the first time when they are faced with the upbringing of their children. Certainly the small families of the west are more readily understood when one has become a parent.

Use and understanding go together. The attempt to reach some limited objective, such as a piped water supply or adequate sanitation in one's village, can make real the knowledge passively acquired in school or by reading ; it may also create a demand for more knowledge, which can be satisfied only by further reading. But the reading, if it is to be more than the casual acquisition of knowledge by a dilettante, must be an adjunct to action. This book tells a number of unfinished stories.   The stories are being continued by the men and women who are working to apply the knowledge that we have.

BOOKS

Books by authors shown in smaller type are either more specialised or more advanced than the rest

CHAPTERS 2 AND 3

DAHLBERG G.
Race, Reason and Rubbish   Allen & Unwin, London, 1942.
Swedish. An introduction to human genetics.

FORD E. B.
The Study of Heredity   Oxford University Press, 1937. British.
An introduction to general genetics.

FORD E. B.
Genetics for Medical Students   Methuen, London, 1942. British.
Mendelian genetics and medicine.

KALMUS H.
Genetics   Penguin Books, London, 1948. British.
Fundamentals of genetics, and their applications to man and to domestic plants and animals.

ROBERTS J. A. F.
Introduction to Medical Genetics   Oxford University Press, 1940.
British.

SCHEINFELD A.
You and Heredity   Chatto & Windus, London, 1939. American.
Easy to read ; covers a very wide field.

WADDINGTON C. H.
An Introduction to Modern Genetics   Allen & Unwin, London.
1939. British.   A textbook for students covering systematic genetics, evolutionary theory, chromosomes and the gene, applied and human genetics.

CHAPTER 4

CORNER G. W.
Ourselves Unborn   Cornell University Press, 1946. American.
Exceptionally readable lectures covering human evolution as well as development.

CORNER G. W.
The Hormones in Human Reproduction   Princeton University Press, 1942. American. Human reproduction and sexual development, with special reference to the role of hormones.

GUTTMACHER A. F.
The Story of Human Birth   Sigma, London, 1949. American.
Wise, witty and entertaining, on all that parents most need to know about pregnancy and birth.

Chapter 5

CLARK W. E. LE GROS
History of the Primates   British Museum, London, 1949. British.
An up-to-date, lucid and straightforward account by an authority on Primate evolution.

HOWELLS O.
Mankind So Far   Doubleday, New York, and Sigma, London, 1945. American. A full and entertaining account of human evolution, written before the recent important discoveries in Africa.

WEIDENREICH H.
Apes, Giants and Men   Chicago University Press, 1946. American.
Lectures, partly on questions still controversial among experts.

Chapters 6 and 7

BENEDICT R.
Race and Racism   Routledge, London, 1942. American.
A short book by a social anthropologist.

DINGWALL J.
Racial Pride and Prejudice   Watts, London, 1946. British.
A survey, by nations, of the relationships between members of different groups.

HALDANE J. B. S.
Heredity and Politics   Allen & Unwin, London, 1938. British.
Lectures on "nature and nurture", eugenics, and "race".

HALDANE J. B. S.
New Paths in Genetics   Allen & Unwin, London, 1941. British.
Lectures, of which the first, on the principles of genetics, is exceptionally valuable.

HUXLEY J. S. and HADDON A. C.
We Europeans   Cape, London, 1935. British.
The main facts of "race" differences, by a biologist and a physical anthropologist.

KLEINBERG O.
Race Differences   Harper, New York, 1935. American.
A comprehensive but concise survey of the facts of physical, mental and social differences.

MORANT G. M.
The Races of Central Europe   Allen & Unwin, London, 1939.
British. A brief, easily understood statement of the true facts.

Chapter 8

BLACKBURN J.
The Framework of Human Behaviour   Kegan Paul, London, 1947.
A discussion of sex, race, national and class differences by a social psychologist.

GRAY J. L.
The Nation's Intelligence   Watts, London, 1936. British.
Discusses the distribution in Britain of the type of ability measured by intelligence tests.

LEYBOURNE G. G. AND WHITE K.
Education and the Birth-rate   Cape, London, 1940. British.
The economics of education and of the bringing up of children.

MAGUINESS O. D.
Environment and Heredity   Nelson, London, 1940. British.
An elementary account based on the biological facts in their application to man.

TYLER L. E.
The Psychology of Human Differences   Appleton-Century,
New York, 1947. American. A text-book for students.

Chapter 9

LUETKENS C.
Women and a New Society   Nicholson & Watson, London, 1946.
British. Heavily illustrated, short survey of the place of women in English society.

MEAD M.
Male and Female   Gollancz, London, 1950. American.
An anthropologist's view.

SCHEINFELD A.
Women and Men   Harcourt, New York, 1943. American.
Comprehensive, simply written.

WILLIAMS G.
Women and Work   Nicholson & Watson, London, 1945. British.
Heavily illustrated, short summary of the facts and problems of women as wage earners.

Chapter 10

CHILDE G.
Man Makes Himself   Watts, London, 1941. British.
Short summary of the origin of agriculture and cities by a distinguished archæologist.

CLARK G.
Savagery to Civilisation   Cobbett, London, 1946. British.
Short, clearly written.

CURWEN C.
Plough and Pasture   Cobbett, London, 1947. British.
Short history of agriculture.

LILLEY S.
Men, Machines and History · Cobbett, London, 1948. British.
History of inventions in relation to social change.

Chapters 11 and 12

CLARK F. Le GROS
Feeding the Human Family   Sigma, London, 1948. British.
A discussion on the scientific and economic problems of world food.

DRUMMOND J. and WILBRAHAM A.
The Englishman's Food   Cape, London, 1939. British.
A history, full of fascinating detail.

ELTON C.
Animal Ecology   Sidgwick & Jackson, London, 1947. British.
An outstanding, short textbook.

GLESINGER E.
The Coming Age of Wood   Sigma, London, 1950. American.
An outstanding, short textbook

GRAHAM E. H.
Natural Principles of Land Use   Oxford, New York, 1944.
American. Short, beautifully illustrated, well documented survey of applied ecology.

McCARRISON R.
Nutrition and National Health   Faber, London, 1944. British.
Lectures, including a description of experiments on Indian national diets, and a survey from a medical point of view.

MARRACK J. R.
Food and Planning   Gollancz, London, 1942. British.
The biochemistry of nutrition, dietary surveys, experiments on human feeding and the economics of food.

ORR J. B.
Food, Health and Income   Macmillan, London, 1936. British.
The most famous of all nutrition surveys.

OSBORN F.
Our Plundered Planet   Faber, London, 1948. American.
The misuse of natural resources and the remedies.

U.S. DEPARTMENT OF AGRICULTURE
Yearbook 1939   U.S. Government, Washington, 1939. American.
On "Food and life".

CHAPTER 13

SAND R.
Health and Human Progress   Kegan Paul, London, 1935. French.
General survey of social medicine.

SORSBY A.
Medicine and Mankind   Faber, London, 1941. British.
What medical knowledge can do, and how it is often not used where it is most needed.

STEIGLITZ E. J.
A Future for Preventive Medicine   Commonwealth Fund, New York, 1945. American.
Short, deals especially with effects of population changes.

STERN B. J.
Society and Medical Progress   Princeton, 1941. American.
Short history.

TAYLOR S.
Battle for Health   Nicholson & Watson, London, 1944. British.
Simple, short, heavily illustrated.

TITMUSS R. M.
Birth, Poverty and Wealth   Hamish Hamilton, London, 1943.
British. Infant mortality, stillbirth rates, etc., in relation to economic facts.

CHAPTER 14

CARR-SAUNDERS A. M.
World Population   Oxford, 1936. British.
Population problems, and population trends throughout the world.

MYRDAL A.
Nation and Family   Routledge, London, 1945. Swedish.
General discussion of declining fertility in Europe, and detailed account of Swedish experience.

THOMPSON W.
Plenty of People   Jacques Cattell Press, Lancaster, Penn., 1944.
American. Short, popular, comprehensive survey of population problems.

CHAPTER 15

BERNAL J. D.
Science in History   Watts, London, 1950. British.
Short, popular.

BERNAL J. D.
Social Function of Science   Routledge, London, 1939. British.
A standard work.

CROWTHER J. G.
Social Relations of Science   Macmillan, 1941. British.
Historical studies.

DUNHAM B.
Man against Myth   Muller, London, 1948. American.
Debunking of misconceptions about human biology and many other topics,
by a philosopher.

HALL, D. and others
Frustration of Science   Allen & Unwin, London, 1935. British.
Examples by eight authorities.

WADDINGTON C. H.
Scientific Attitude   Penguin, London, 1941. British.
Nature of scientific thought, and relations of science to art and politics.

INDEX

d before a folio number indicates that there is a diagram referring to the subject on the page given. *pl* before a number indicates plate.